Solving Real Problems
with Chemistry

Second Edition

Edited by **John Goodwin, Coastal Carolina University**
David Hanson, Stony Brook University
Troy Wolfskill, Stony Brook University

published by

Pacific Crest

Lisle, IL

Solving Real Problems with Chemistry

Second Edition

Edited by   John Goodwin, Coastal Carolina University
David Hanson, Stony Brook University
Troy Wolfskill, Stony Brook University

Layout, Production, and Cover Design by Denna Hintze-Yates

Copyright © 2012

Pacific Crest
13250 S. Route 59, Unit 104
Plainfield, IL 60585
815-676-3470
www.pcrest.com

ISBN: 978-1-60263-514-2

Table of Contents

Preface: To Students and Instructors

Science students often ask why they are required to study subjects outside their specific field of interest. If your institution is like most, a large proportion of the students in your chemistry class are not chemistry or chemical engineering majors, and may see General Chemistry as one more hoop to jump through on the way to a degree in another major. But, if you look beyond campus, in upper level courses in your major or research labs on campus, you'll find that the separation between sciences is not so tidy as your college catalog would imply. Many scientists actually use a wide variety of tools from other disciplines to solve problems in their specific area. This sort of interdisciplinary approach in science is becoming more common all the time, and it is often necessary to focus on these areas between and across the disciplines to make new discoveries. But, to be able to apply a tool to a new problem is one of the most challenging skills both students and scientists need to acquire.

The intent of *Solving Real Problems with Chemistry* is to help students develop their ability to apply chemistry principles to solve new problems, often within a context that might not seem like chemistry at first. It builds upon a recognized robust pedagogy called Process-Oriented Guided-Inquiry Learning (POGIL) that is widely used to engage students in the learning process and help them master the material through conceptual understanding rather than memorizing patterns for answering traditional questions. It emphasizes building the important skills of information processing, critical and analytical thinking, oral and written communication, teamwork, and metacognition. Extending beyond these fundamental learning levels and skills, *Solving Real Problems with Chemistry* is best used as a follow-up companion to more standard POGIL activities such as those found in *Foundations of Chemistry* by David Hanson (published by Pacific Crest). Activities from *Solving Real Problems with Chemistry* are usually worked by groups of students who are already accustomed to using the POGIL method, and after the corresponding chemistry content has been mastered through the standard activities and other work in the course. We refer to this advanced POGIL pedagogy, which makes use of rich contexts for problem solving, as POGIL-in-Context or POGIL-IC for short.

Each POGIL-IC activity has several parts specifically designed to improve applied problem-solving skills. An **Introduction** to the problem and its context provides important information necessary for appreciating, understanding, and solving the problem. The introduction is followed with the descriptively titled sections **Prerequisite Knowledge, Applying Your New Skills, The Problem, Solve the Problem and Document Your Solution, Does Your Answer Make Sense?, Building Your Problem-Solving Skills, Got It!,** and **References,** that combine to create the stage for the development of problem solving skills.

The statements in **Applying Your New Skills** connect to the two **Got It!** problems at the end of an activity. These problems give students the opportunity to practice transferring their new knowledge and skills to new situations. The first problem uses the same context as the initial problem but changes the focus. The second problem involves the same concepts but these need to be applied in a new context.

Scientists continually look for ways to validate their work to make sure they are on the right track. **Does Your Answer Make Sense?** guides students in this process, which is an important skill to develop because it can improve performance on exams as students find errors before the exam is submitted for scoring.

Metacognition is the key to improvement. Metacognition literally means thinking about *thinking*, and the section **Building Your Problem Solving Skills** helps students reflect on and think about their problem solving process and how to improve it. This is probably the most important section.

A unique feature of the book is a set of **Help** pages that provide a guided-inquiry approach to solving the problem for each activity. These pages are available to the instructors and facilitators as pdf files, and are to be distributed to students as needed during the group problem-solving session. The **Help** pages provide a general problem-solving guide for students who need little or no help as gold-level performers (**Au Help**), a set of critical thinking questions that lead silver-level performers to think about the key issues (**Ag Help**), and a more detailed set of questions for copper-level performers (**Cu Help**). In Cu Help, students essentially work as apprentices following an expert problem solver. All the sections after **Solve the Problem and Document Your Solution** are there to develop and reinforce the problem-solving skills required in the activity.

Problem-solving ability develops over time with practice, so using one of these activities after completing a unit of instruction consistently over a semester or year provides students with the practice and reinforcement necessary for improvement. Using these activities in isolation or without standard POGIL pedagogy is not recommended. Sustained use should raise the bar for performance in problem solving, and also provide necessary tools and motivation for improvement.

Acknowledgments

We gratefully acknowledge the National Science Foundation for financial support of the Collaborative Project, Development of POGIL-IC Modules for General Chemistry DUE 0633191, DUE 0632957, and DUE 0633231). We are also indebted to the POGIL project for offering inspiration, guidance and valuable feedback in creating these advanced POGIL activities. The sustained efforts of Pacific Crest in the support of the POGIL project through Dan Apple (President) and Karl Krumsieg has continued with our project, particularly with the valuable composition and editorial skills of Denna Hintze-Yates.

The contributions of several collaborators must be recognized. Candice Foley, Linda Hobart, Vicky Minderhout Thorsell, Kimberly Lawless, Austin Hitt and Renee Cole have all been invaluable to the project for their insights and development of the pedagogical format and developmental assessment as well as authoring and reviewing activities of others. Contributing co-authors and editors included in the pre-market and first editions are:

Darlene Slusher	Coastal Carolina University
Tom Gilbert	Northeastern University
Linda Hobart	Finger Lakes Community College
Tracy Suggs	Vestal Senior High School
Vicki Petro	Stony Brook University
Katherine Grobsky	Coastal Carolina University
Jill Barker	James Wood High School
Jennifer Stauffer	Hopkins School
Jamie Benigna	Roeper School
Brett Simpson	Coastal Carolina University
Austin Hitt	Coastal Carolina University
Cheryl Coolidge	Colby-Sawyer College
Renee Cole	University of Central Missouri
Fred Yost	Carteret Community College
Rong Chen	Stony Brook University
Debra Rust	Stony Brook University
Candice Foley	Suffolk County Community College
Richard Lumpkin	Lamar University
Vicky Minderhout Thorsell	Seattle University

We would also like to thank these additional participants in the POGIL-IC project who authored additional activities and participated in the development of the pedagogical format:

T. J. Anderson	Francis Marion University
Julia Baker	Columbia College
Phil Bennett	Santa Fe Community College
Kathy Bowdring	Langley High School
Tracy Cheatham	Central Carolina Community College
Patricia Christie	Massachusetts Institute of Technology
David Cunningham	University of Massachusetts, Lowell
Peggy Geiger	Gaston College
Robin Lasey	Arkansas Tech University
Philip Palko	Indiana High School
David Parkin	Adelphi University
Jerry Sarquis	Miami University, Oxford
Gail Webster	Guilford College
Kathryn Yost	Carteret Community College

Expert reviews of activities were provided by:

Julie Abrahamson	University of North Dakota
Anne Falke	Worcester State College
Michael Garoutte	Missouri Southern State University
Mildred Hall	Clark State Community College
Bruce Heyen	Tabor College
Richard Lumpkin	Lamar University
Libbie Pelter	Purdue University Calumet
Marty Perry	Ouchita Baptist University
Stephen Prilliman	Harding Charter Preparatory High School
Susan Shadle	Boise State University
Mary Walczak	St. Olaf College
Lou Wojcinski	Kansas State University

John Goodwin is indebted to Coastal Carolina University for a Scholarly Reassignment devoted to the original development of the pedagogy, and CCU students in CHEM 111 and CHEM 112 for enduring early versions of activities and providing important feedback.

ACTIVITY 1

CHEAP GAS: IS IT WORTH THE DRIVE?

College students need to be frugal because they usually have lots of expenses and little income. It is expensive to have a car, so saving a few cents, or even more, on each gallon of gasoline purchased can make a real difference in a budget.

Gas prices are not the same in all parts of a community. Some stations are always the price leaders, trading off cost for volume, and the cheapest gas is usually not near an expressway or affluent neighborhood. You can find gas prices in your area at **www.gasbuddy.com**

When is it worthwhile to make a special trip across town to buy gas at that one station that is cheaper than all the rest?

This activity will help you learn what must be done to answer that question. In the process, you also will begin to learn how to analyze quantitative (numerical) problems that have several parts. In addition, you will practice using units, unit analysis, and unit conversion. All of these things are extremely important in solving problems that you will encounter later involving atoms, molecules, and chemical reactions.

 ## PREREQUISITE KNOWLEDGE

Before beginning this activity, you should be able to

- Identify the units associated with quantities like length or distance, time, and volume

- Convert from one unit to another (e.g., kilometers to miles, minutes to hours, and liters to gallons)

- Use unit or dimensional analysis (e.g., miles per gallon) to obtain the units associated with a numerical answer or to show that the arithmetic used is correct

APPLYING YOUR NEW SKILLS

Upon completing this activity, you should be able to

- Analyze gas prices at different stations and identify when it is reasonable to drive some distance to purchase gas

- Analyze information about two products and decide which one is the better buy

Contributed by John Goodwin, Coastal Carolina University
Revised by Linda Hobart, Finger Lakes Community College
Revised by Vicki Petro and David Hanson, Stony Brook University

THE PROBLEM

The gas station with the cheapest gas in your area has been found. The relevant information about this station is given below. If you drive to the station with the cheapest gas, will you end up saving or losing money when you consider all the factors listed below? Support your answer with calculations.

To answer this question, you need to compare *all* the costs of using the station next door with *all* the costs of driving to the station with the cheapest gas. If you need additional information, look it up or make assumptions, as appropriate.

i INFORMATION

- Driving distance to the cheap gas station is 5.4 mi.

- Gas costs $3.51/gal next door, but $0.90/liter at the cheap station, which is located in Metric Village

- You could earn $7.50/hour at your job instead of driving to get gas

- It takes 3.5 minutes to fill your tank with gas

- Your car can travel 27.6 miles on one gallon of gasoline

- You have just enough gas to drive to the cheap station, and your tank can presently hold an additional 15.6 gallons

- You have to make a round trip

- Assume your average driving speed to and from the gas station is 45 mph. Average speed is equal to total distance traveled divided by the time it took to travel that distance.

Solving Real Problems with Chemistry

✔ SOLVE THE PROBLEM AND DOCUMENT YOUR SOLUTION

Name: _____

Other Team Members: _____

Date: _____ Activity Title: _____

Level of Help used to solve this problem by the team: **none** ☐ **Au** ☐ **Ag** ☐ **Cu** ☐

Work with your team to solve the problem. Your instructor can provide three levels of help called gold, silver, and copper. *Au Help* presents a strategy that resembles the way experts think when they solve problems. The use of this strategy is illustrated and prompted to different degrees in *Ag Help* and *Cu Help*. As the semester progresses, you should move through these stages of *Help* to grow your problem solving skills. Your instructor will tell you what you need to do to document your solution. One method would be to provide the information requested in *Au Help*.

? DOES YOUR ANSWER MAKE SENSE?

1. Which two factors are most important in determining where to purchase the gas? Explain.

2. Is the amount of money saved or lost reasonable? Explain why you think so.

3. Do the units in your answer make sense? Show that they follow from your calculations.

BUILDING YOUR PROBLEM-SOLVING SKILLS

You will be able to complete the *Got It!* section, which comes next, more efficiently, and you will do better on exams if you take a few minutes now to improve your problem-solving skills. Communicating the steps in your problem solution to others and thinking back on the problem that you just completed will help you to improve.

1. Share your team's problem solution with your class as called upon by the instructor.

2. Identify the most important thing you learned today about either the problem-solving process or a problem-solving skill that will help you solve new problems.

3. Consider whether you could solve this problem using a more efficient procedure so you can answer a similar exam question more quickly. If you find one, describe this more efficient procedure.

4. Identify whether there are any issues or assumptions contained in the problem and its solution that would limit using the same procedure for other problems.

5. Identify features of this problem and its solution that could apply to other problems.

1. What would the price of gas have to be in Metric Village for you to save $1.00 when you fill up with gas?

2. A small keg of imported beer costs $19.95 and contains 5.0 L. A case of the same beer costs $31.99 and contains twenty-four 12 oz bottles. Which is the better buy? Explain why. (These are actual prices obtained from a local beverage store.)

ACTIVITY 2

ARE HOMEOPATHIC MEDICINES ONLY PLACEBOS?

Homeopathic medicine was developed in the late 1700s by Samuel Hahnemann, a German physician, who thought that bloodletting, leeching, blistering, and other harsh physical and chemical procedures that were practiced at the time did more harm than good. Hahnemann's idea was that a disease could be treated with small amounts of a medication that in large amounts would produce symptoms similar to those of the disease. The name homeopathy therefore is derived from the Greek words *homoios* meaning *similar* or *like* and *pathos* meaning *suffering*.

Homeopathic medicines are naturally occurring substances found in plants, minerals, or animals. Practitioners of homeopathy believe that the effectiveness of the homeopathic medication increases with dilution. Therefore, doses of the active ingredient are prepared by repeatedly diluting a solution by a factor of 10, 100, 1000, or even more. [3,4] For example, a 2X dilution would be prepared by diluting 1.0 mL of pure solute to make 10.0 mL of 1X solution, then diluting 1.0 mL of the 1X solution to make 10.0 mL of a more dilute 2X solution.

A *placebo* is an inert medication given to simulate treatment. Placebos sometimes have a positive effect because they can affect the mental state of a patient, who thinks the disease is being treated. At some level of dilution, a homeopathic medicine becomes a placebo because no active ingredient remains in the volume of solution ingested. Believers, however, think that the medication can be effective because the active ingredient has left an imprint or spirit-like essence that stimulates the body to heal itself.

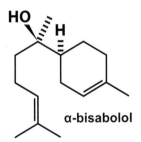

Chamomile, a plant in the sunflower family, has been used as a homeopathic medicine for thousands of years, and is one of the more popular natural remedies on the market today. It is often used to treat symptoms related to sleep disorders, digestion conditions, cramps, skin infections, inflammation, and teething pains. The main compound in chamomile that is responsible for its anti-inflammatory properties is α-bisabolol. Your task in this activity is to determine how many molecules of α-bisabolol remain in a highly diluted dose of chamomile.

 # PREREQUISITE KNOWLEDGE

Before beginning this activity, you should be able to

- Convert between mass, moles, and number of molecules
- Convert between mass and volume given the density
- Determine molar mass given a chemical formula
- Define mass percent of a substance in solution

Contributed by Darlene L. Slusher and Katherine E. Grobsky, Coastal Carolina University

APPLYING YOUR NEW SKILLS

Upon completing this activity, you should be able to

- Use density, molar mass, and mass percent to determine the number of molecules of an active ingredient in a given volume of a homeopathic medicine

- Determine the number of molecules of one component in a mixture given the masses of substances present

THE PROBLEM

A 6X chamomile remedy recommends that adults take a 1.0 mL dose. How many α-bisabolol molecules, if any, are present in each 1.0 mL dose of the remedy?

You may find the following information helpful:

- A 6X homeopathic medicine means that a 1-to-10 dilution has been repeated 6 times, leaving the active ingredient concentration one millionth the original concentration. The "X" represents the Roman numeral 10.

- The density of chamomile is 0.91 g/mL

- α-bisabolol is $C_{15}H_{26}O$ and has a molar mass of 222.37 g/mol

- Chamomile is a mixture of many compounds. Assume that 0.25% of the mass of chamomile is α-bisabolol, which is typical if the remedy is made from crushed dried flowers[5]

chamomile

SOLVE THE PROBLEM AND DOCUMENT YOUR SOLUTION

Name: _____

Other Team Members: _____

Date: _____ Activity Title: _____

Level of Help used to solve this problem by the team: *none* ☐   *Au* ☐   *Ag* ☐   *Cu* ☐

Work with your team to solve the problem. Your instructor can provide three levels of help called gold, silver, and copper. *Au Help* presents a strategy that resembles the way experts think when they solve problems. The use of this strategy is illustrated and prompted to different degrees in *Ag Help* and *Cu Help*. As the semester progresses, you should move through these stages of *Help* to grow your problem solving skills. Your instructor will tell you what you need to do to document your solution. One method would be to provide the information requested in *Au Help*.

? DOES YOUR ANSWER MAKE SENSE?

1. Show how unit analysis reveals that your answer has the correct units of *molecules*.

2. Should your answer be larger or smaller than one mole? Explain why. Is it?

BUILDING YOUR PROBLEM-SOLVING SKILLS

You will be able to complete the *Got It!* section, which comes next, more efficiently, and you will do better on exams if you take a few minutes now to improve your problem-solving skills. Communicating the steps in your problem solution to others and thinking back on the problem that you just completed will help you to improve.

1. Share your team's problem solution with your class as called upon by the instructor.

2. Identify the most important thing you learned today about either the problem-solving process or a problem-solving skill that will help you solve new problems.

3. Consider whether you could solve this problem using a more efficient procedure so you can answer a similar exam question more quickly. If you find one, describe this more efficient procedure.

4. Identify whether there are any issues or assumptions contained in the problem and its solution that would limit using the same procedure for other problems.

5. Identify features of this problem and its solution that could apply to other problems.

1. Another ingredient in chamomile that has an anti-inflammatory effect is chamazulene ($C_{14}H_{16}$). If chamazulene comprises approximately 1% of the mass of chamomile, how many molecules of chamazulene are in each 1.0 mL dose of 6X chamomile remedy?

2. A particular manufacturer of phosphoric acid pellets,[6] marketed as "phosphoricum acidum," sells a variety of concentrations including 12C, where "C" represents the Roman numeral 100. 12C then means the mass of H_3PO_4 in the pellet has been reduced by a factor of 1/100 twelve times so the result is: $\dfrac{1}{\left(10^2\right)^{12}}$ the total mass. (The rest of the mass is filler.) The pellets have an average mass of 0.022125 g.

How many pellets would you need to take in order to expect to get one molecule of H_3PO_4?

REFERENCES

[1] National Institutes of Health Medline Plus. http://www.nlm.nih.gov/medlineplus/druginfo/natural/patient-chamomile.html (accessed June 3, 2008).

[2] Budavari, S., O'Neil, M. J., Smith, A., Heckelman, P. E., Kinneary, J. F., Eds. The Merck Index: An Encyclopedia of Chemicals, Drugs, and Biologicals, 13th ed.; Merck & Company: Whitehouse Station, NJ, 2001; entry 1241.

[3] Stehlin, I. Homeopathy: Real Medicine or Empty Promises, *FDA Consumer* [Online] **1996**, *30*, pp 15-19.

[4] Homeopathic Potency and Dilution. http://www.ritecare.com/homeopathic/guide_potency.asp (accessed June 13, 2008).

[5] Falzari, L.M., and Menary, R.C. Australian Government Rural Industries Research and Development Corporation. www.rirdc.gov.au/reports/EOI/02-156.pdf (accessed June 12, 2008). Chamomile for Oil and Dried Flowers, Publication No 02/156, RIRDC Project No UT-28A, February 2003.

[6] Phosphoricum Acidum—Homeopahy. http://www.abchomeopathy.com/r.php/Ph-ac (accessed June 13, 2008).

ACTIVITY 3

FORMULATING A FERTILIZER

Many types of fertilizers are used for household plants, lawn care, gardening, and agriculture. Some of these are composed of simple inorganic compounds that are mixed together. These compounds provide three elements that are major plant nutrients: nitrogen (N), phosphorus (P), and potassium (K). Different fertilizers contain different proportions of these elements.

The amounts of these nutrients present in any fertilizer are identified on the label in the order N-P-K, e.g., 10-10-10, 20-5-5, or 5-10-5, but contrary to what you might expect, these numbers are not directly related to the amounts of N, P, and K in the fertilizer. These numbers identify the *mass percent* of N, P_2O_5, and K_2O.

A fertilizer high in nitrogen content is used to promote top growth in plants. Such fertilizers are commonly used on lawns. A fertilizer high in phosphorous promotes root growth, and one high in potassium

promotes the development of flowers. Using too much nitrogen with house and garden plants usually produces tall, lanky plants that tend not to flower or bear much fruit.

As part of your summer job at a local garden shop, your task is to prepare an optimal fertilizer for bonsai plants. Since bonsai are compact flowering plants, the optimum composition is 5-10-5, and you must determine the amounts of nitrogen, phosphorous, and potassium-containing compounds needed to prepare a 5-10-5 fertilizer.

✔ PREREQUISITE KNOWLEDGE

Before beginning this activity, you should be able to

- Convert from kilograms to grams

- Calculate the molar mass of a compound given the molecular formula

- Determine the mass percent of an element in a compound given the molecular formula

- Use percent composition by mass and total mass to calculate the mass of a component in a mixture

- Use inorganic nomenclature to determine molecular formulas of compounds

Contributed by John Goodwin, Coastal Carolina University
Revised by Darlene Slusher, Coastal Carolina University, and David Hanson, Stony Brook University
Edited by Jill Barker, James Wood High School, Jennifer Stauffer, Hopkins School, and Jamie Benigna, Roeper School

APPLYING YOUR NEW SKILLS

Upon completing this activity, you should be able to

- Use NPK values for a fertilizer to determine the amount (mass and moles) of nitrogen, phosphorous, and potassium in the fertilizer

- Determine the masses of compounds needed to furnish the elements required to synthesize a given substance

THE PROBLEM

Your task is to prepare 1.00 kg of a 5-10-5 fertilizer for bonsai trees. The 5-10-5 composition means that the fertilizer contains the equivalent of 5% N, 10% P_2O_5, and 5% K_2O by mass, plus some additional inert filler to total 1.00 kg.

Elements in the fertilizer can only be added as parts of compounds. For each element (N, P, and K), you have one compound available: ammonium nitrate is the source of N, calcium hydrogen phosphate is the source of P, and potassium sulfate is the source of K.

How many grams of ammonium nitrate, calcium hydrogen phosphate, and potassium sulfate are needed to make 1.00 kg of the 5-10-5 fertilizer? (Assume that these percentages are exact. Note that the mass of the fertilizer includes some inert filler.)

To answer this question, break the problem into parts and solve each part separately. (This strategy generally helps in solving problems.) First, determine how many grams of N, P, and K are present in 1.00 kg of the 5-10-5 fertilizer. Then determine how many grams of each of the compounds that you have are needed to provide these elements.

A Dwarf Japanese Juniper
(*Juniperus procumbens* 'Nana') bonsai on display at the United States National Arboretum. Image from Wikipedia: Ragesoss

SOLVE THE PROBLEM AND DOCUMENT YOUR SOLUTION

Name: _____

Other Team Members: _____

Date: _____ Activity Title: _____

Level of Help used to solve this problem by the team: *none* ☐   *Au* ☐   *Ag* ☐   *Cu* ☐

Work with your team to solve the problem. Your instructor can provide three levels of help called gold, silver, and copper. *Au Help* presents a strategy that resembles the way experts think when they solve problems. The use of this strategy is illustrated and prompted to different degrees in *Ag Help* and *Cu Help*. As the semester progresses, you should move through these stages of *Help* to grow your problem solving skills. Your instructor will tell you what you need to do to document your solution. One method would be to provide the information requested in *Au Help*.

1. What is the total mass of the ammonium nitrate, calcium hydrogen phosphate, and potassium sulfate needed to make this fertilizer?

2. Is the total mass reasonable? (If it is greater than 1 kg, is that reasonable? If it is less than 1 kg, does the total have to equal 1 kg?) Explain.

BUILDING YOUR PROBLEM-SOLVING SKILLS

You will be able to complete the *Got It!* section, which comes next, more efficiently, and you will do better on exams if you take a few minutes now to improve your problem-solving skills. Communicating the steps in your problem solution to others and thinking back on the problem that you just completed will help you to improve.

1. Share your team's problem solution with your class as called upon by the instructor.

2. Identify the most important thing you learned today about either the problem-solving process or a problem-solving skill that will help you solve new problems.

3. Consider whether you could solve this problem using a more efficient procedure so you can answer a similar exam question more quickly. If you find one, describe this more efficient procedure.

4. Identify whether there are any issues or assumptions contained in the problem and its solution that would limit using the same procedure for other problems.

5. Identify features of this problem and its solution that could apply to other problems.

1. Determine the mass and number of moles of N, P, and K present in 1 kg of a 10-20-20 fertilizer.

2. From 1962 to 1982, the composition of the U.S. penny was 95% copper and 5% zinc by weight. The average mass of the penny was 3.1 g. The main source of copper is chalcopyrite ($CuFeS_2$), and for the purposes of this question, you should assume that the source of zinc is smithsonite (zinc carbonate).

   a. How many grams of chalcopyrite are required to obtain the copper needed for one penny?

   b. How many grams of smithsonite are required to obtain the zinc needed for one penny?

SUBSTITUTE BAKING SODA FOR BAKING POWDER

Baking powder and baking soda may seem interchangeable to anyone who hasn't baked cookies, brownies, muffins, or biscuits. Both are used as leavening agents since they can react to form carbon dioxide gas, making breads rise. Baking soda is pure sodium bicarbonate, $NaHCO_3$, but baking powder is a mixture of sodium bicarbonate and a solid acid that dissolves in water. When sodium bicarbonate reacts with acid, carbon dioxide gas is formed. Baking soda alone does not produce carbon dioxide and only reacts to produce this gas if there are acids in other ingredients in the recipe. Baking powder alone can produce carbon dioxide because both reactants needed to produce the gas are present in the mixture. Cooks know that baking soda with added cream of tartar makes a good substitute for baking powder. In this activity you'll examine the chemistry of this substitution as a food chemist might.

Figure 1 A "volcano" demonstration uses the reaction of baking soda with vinegar.

PREREQUISITE KNOWLEDGE

Before beginning this activity, you should be able to

- Recognize and write the products of an acid-base neutralization reaction

- Write the formulas for ionic compounds

- Calculate the molar mass of a compound

- Use a balanced chemical reaction equation and the given mass of one reactant to calculate the needed mass of another reactant

APPLYING YOUR NEW SKILLS

After completing this activity, you should be able to

- Recognize that carbonic acid is unstable, decomposing to water and carbon dioxide

- Explain that reactants are often interchangeable. In this case you'll see that a base can be neutralized by many different acids.

- Add balanced reaction equations together to get a new, overall reaction equation

- Use the mole concept to relate masses of reactants or products by using their formula masses

Contributed by John Goodwin, Coastal Carolina University

Baking soda is pure sodium bicarbonate, $NaHCO_3$, which dissolves and dissociates in water into the sodium ion and the bicarbonate ion. As most students know from demonstrations in grade school or at home, it can be mixed with vinegar for a rapid and entertaining chemical reaction that generates carbon dioxide gas bubbling out of the reaction mixture. The overall reaction can be written as:

$$CH_3COO\underline{H}(aq) + Na^+(aq) + HCO_3^-(aq) \rightarrow Na^+(aq) + CH_3COO^-(aq) + H_2O(l) + CO_2(g)$$

in which the sodium ion is a spectator ion.

Baking soda or baking powder can be used in recipes as a leavening agent—that is, to produce carbon dioxide gas to make dough or batter rise. Recipes using baking *soda* must include a separate acidic ingredient such as buttermilk or vinegar. Recipes that do not include the separate addition of an acidic ingredient usually require baking *powder* instead. Baking powder has a solid organic acid mixed in with the baking soda, so that when the mixture is dissolved, the acid and sodium bicarbonate react with each other. While commercial baking powder involves slightly more complicated chemistry, a good substitute for baking powder can be made by adding baking soda to an acid such as potassium hydrogen tartrate (potassium bitartrate or cream of tartar). The formula for potassium hydrogen tartrate is $K\underline{H}C_4H_4O_6$.

Your task is to devise a suitable substitute for baking powder by calculating the mass of cream of tartar in grams required to react with 10.00 g of baking soda. There should be enough cream of tartar added so that all of the baking soda will react to make carbon dioxide gas, but no more cream of tartar than that.

SOLVE THE PROBLEM AND DOCUMENT YOUR SOLUTION

Name: _____

Other Team Members: _____

Date: _____   Activity Title: _____

Level of Help used to solve this problem by the team: **none** ☐   *Au* ☐   *Ag* ☐   *Cu* ☐

Work with your team to solve the problem. Your instructor can provide three levels of help called gold, silver, and copper. *Au Help* presents a strategy that resembles the way experts think when they solve problems. The use of this strategy is illustrated and prompted to different degrees in *Ag Help* and *Cu Help*. As the semester progresses, you should move through these stages of *Help* to grow your problem solving skills. Your instructor will tell you what you need to do to document your solution. One method would be to provide the information requested in *Au Help*.

? DOES YOUR ANSWER MAKE SENSE?

1. What units do you need for your final answer? Did you obtain the correct units in your calculation? Explain.

2. Based on your experiences with cooking or intuition, about what mass of cream of tartar is needed? Explain your logic. Is your calculated mass somewhat close to that?

BUILDING YOUR PROBLEM-SOLVING SKILLS

You will be able to complete the *Got It!* section, which comes next, more efficiently, and you will do better on exams if you take a few minutes now to improve your problem-solving skills. Communicating the steps in your problem solution to others and thinking back on the problem that you just completed will help you to improve.

1. Share your team's problem solution with your class as called upon by the instructor.

2. Identify the most important thing you learned about problem solving today that will help you solve new problems.

3. Consider whether you could solve this problem using a more efficient procedure so you can answer a similar exam question more quickly. If you find one, describe this more efficient procedure.

4. Identify whether there are any issues or assumptions contained in the problem and its solution that would limit using the same procedure for other problems.

5. Identify features of this problem and its solution that could apply to other problems.

1. A cook who wants to substitute baking soda for baking powder in a recipe finds
    no cream of tartar in the pantry, but plenty of vinegar. If the vinegar is a 5.15%
    solution of acetic acid by mass, how many grams of vinegar would be needed to
    react with 15.00 grams of baking soda?

2. A lake can be made acidic by the run-off from open mines or acid rain. One way to temporarily
    neutralize the acid in a lake is by "liming" or adding calcium carbonate, $CaCO_3$. Although the actual
    water chemistry is more complicated than what is described here, let's say that a small lake contains
    500 million liters of water, and that each liter of water contains 0.0250 grams of sulfuric acid (H_2SO_4),
    a diprotic acid, which is run-off from a nearby mine. How much calcium carbonate, in kilograms,
    should be added to the lake in order to completely neutralize the acid by making calcium sulfate and
    carbon dioxide?

NEUTRALIZING WASHING SODA FOR DISPOSAL

Sodium carbonate (Na_2CO_3), also known as washing soda, is the sodium salt of carbonic acid. It is caustic and a relatively strong base with a variety of uses. It is used in making glass, to adjust the pH of swimming pools, and to remove flesh in taxidermy, among other things. Joe the Plumber uses washing soda to remove oil and grease from his tools. Being responsible and safety conscious, he wants to neutralize this base with acidic vinegar before disposing of his waste solutions. He needs your help to determine how much vinegar he needs to use.

Background: Why Vinegar Neutralizes Washing Soda!

Washing soda is sodium carbonate, Na_2CO_3, which dissolves and dissociates in water. One molecule of sodium carbonate produces two sodium ions and one carbonate ion in solution. When mixed with vinegar, sodium carbonate produces a chemical reaction that generates carbon dioxide gas, water, and sodium acetate, which is another salt. The active ingredient in vinegar is acetic acid, which has the formula CH_3COOH, where the acidic proton is shown in red. One carbonate ion uses the acidic proton from two acetic acid molecules to form carbonic acid (H_2CO_3), which decomposes into carbon dioxide and water. The transfer of protons from an acid to a base is an acid-base neutralization reaction.

We can break this overall reaction into four steps: loss of the acidic proton by acetic acid, gain of a proton by carbonate to produce hydrogen carbonate, gain of a second proton by hydrogen carbonate to produce carbonic acid, and finally decomposition of the carbonic acid.

(1) $2CH_3COOH(aq) \rightarrow 2CH_3COO^-(aq) + 2H^+(aq)$

(2) $H^+(aq) + CO_3^{2-}(aq) \rightarrow HCO_3^-(aq)$

(3) $H^+(aq) + HCO_3^-(aq) \rightarrow H_2CO_3(aq)$

(4) $H_2CO_3(aq) \rightarrow H_2O(l) + CO_2(g)$

Reactions 1 through 3 can be added together to give the overall neutralization reaction (5):

(5) $2CH_3COOH(aq) + CO_3^{2-}(aq) \rightarrow 2CH_3COO^-(aq) + H_2CO_3(aq)$

Reactions 4 and 5, when added together, give a new overall reaction:

(6) $2CH_3COOH(aq) + CO_3^{2-}(aq) \rightarrow 2CH_3COO^-(aq) + H_2O(l) + CO_2(g)$

Contributed by David Hanson, Stony Brook University

PREREQUISITE KNOWLEDGE

Before beginning this activity, you should be able to

- Write the molecular formulas from the names of ionic compounds

- Identify and write the products of an acid-base neutralization reaction, e.g., acetic acid reacting with sodium carbonate

- Calculate the molar mass of a compound

- Use a balanced chemical reaction equation to calculate amount of one reactant needed to react with another reactant

- Determine amount of a reactant in solution from the volume and molar concentration of the solution

 # APPLYING YOUR NEW SKILLS

After completing this activity, you should be able to

- Determine how much vinegar is needed to react with a given amount of baking soda (sodium hydrogen carbonate)

- Determine the amount of acid or base that is needed in an acid-base neutralization reaction

 # THE PROBLEM

Joe the Plumber dissolves 54 g of washing soda in water to make 250 mL of his degreasing solution. Your task is to help Joe determine the minimum volume of vinegar that he needs to use to neutralize one liter of his degreasing solution. Assume that vinegar has a density of 1.01 g/mL and contains 5.0% acetic acid by mass.

Joe's Custom Degreasing Solution
(washing soda & water)

Name: _____

Other Team Members: _____

Date: _____ Activity Title: _____

Level of Help used to solve this problem by the team: *none* ☐   *Au* ☐   *Ag* ☐   *Cu* ☐

Work with your team to solve the problem. Your instructor can provide three levels of help called gold, silver, and copper. *Au Help* presents a strategy that resembles the way experts think when they solve problems. The use of this strategy is illustrated and prompted to different degrees in *Ag Help* and *Cu Help*. As the semester progresses, you should move through these stages of *Help* to grow your problem solving skills. Your instructor will tell you what you need to do to document your solution. One method would be to provide the information requested in *Au Help*.

? DOES YOUR ANSWER MAKE SENSE?

1. What units do you need for your final answer? Did you obtain the correct units in your calculation? Explain.

2. What volume of vinegar contains a mass of acetic acid equal to the mass of washing soda in the degreasing solution? Is your carefully calculated volume comparable to this estimate, or are they widely different? If they are widely different, why is it reasonable for the values to be so different?

BUILDING YOUR PROBLEM-SOLVING SKILLS

You will be able to complete the *Got It!* section, which comes next, more efficiently, and you will do better on exams if you take a few minutes now to improve your problem-solving skills. Communicating the steps in your problem solution to others and thinking back on the problem that you just completed will help you to improve.

1. Share your team's problem solution with your class as called upon by the instructor.

2. Identify the most important thing you learned about problem solving today that will help you solve new problems.

3. Consider whether you could solve this problem using a more efficient procedure so you can answer a similar exam question more quickly. If you find one, describe this more efficient procedure.

4. Identify whether there are any issues or assumptions contained in the problem and its solution that would limit using the same procedure for other problems.

5. Identify features of this problem and its solution that could apply to other problems.

1. A cook wants to use vinegar to react with baking soda (sodium hydrogen carbonate) in a bread recipe to produce carbon dioxide, which makes the bread light and fluffy. If the vinegar is a 5.25% solution of acetic acid by mass, what volume of vinegar would be needed to react with 18.00 grams of baking soda? Assume the density of vinegar is the same as that of water.

2. Chlorine reacts with water to produce hydrochloric acid. Suppose 2.5 kg of chlorine were added to an olympic-sized swimming pool. How many grams of calcium carbonate would be needed to neutralize all of the hydrochloric acid that might be produced by this amount of chlorine?

KEEPING WARM WITH CARBON-BASED FUELS

People have used carbon-based fuels ever since the first campfire. Coal was the first widely used fossil fuel since it could simply be dug from the ground and burned. The use of petroleum as a source of liquid fuels such as gasoline, diesel and heating oil, and kerosene requires complicated separation and processing methods that rely heavily on chemistry and chemical engineering expertise. Natural gas and propane are particularly desirable as fuels because they produce little other than carbon dioxide and water when burned.

This activity focuses on the relative merits of these carbon-based fuels as a source of heat. Heat is defined as energy that is transferred due to a temperature difference. The maximum amount of heat that can be obtained

in combustion of a fuel at constant pressure is the change in enthalpy, ΔH, associated with that reaction. The merit of a fuel can be defined in terms of several quantities: fuel value (the energy produced per gram), energy density (the energy produced per milliliter), economic value (the energy produced per dollar), and environmental value (the energy produced per mole of CO_2 product).

Fuel value is important in aviation where keeping the mass of an aircraft low is critical. Energy density, which can mean more miles per tank, is important in applications where fuel storage space is limited, such as in race cars or long-haul trucks. Economic value is important for consumers concerned about getting the greatest value for their money and environmental value is important because the emission of carbon dioxide has an impact on the environment.

PREREQUISITE KNOWLEDGE

Before beginning this activity, you should be able to

- Convert between units

- Use unit analysis (also called *dimensional analysis* or *factor analysis*) in calculations

- Complete and balance chemical reaction equations

- Calculate standard enthalpies of reaction from standard enthalpies of formation for reactants and products

- Use heat capacities to relate changes in temperature to energy flow

Contributed by David Hanson, Stony Brook University with suggestions from Libbie S. W. Pelter, Purdue U./ Calumet, Tom Gilbert, Northeastern University, and John Goodwin, Coastal Carolina University

● APPLYING YOUR NEW SKILLS

Upon completing this activity, you should be able to

- Apply chemical principles to decide which fuel provides the most energy on the basis of mass, volume, price, or other measure

- Identify parameters for chemical reactions to produce or absorb energy on the basis of some given criteria

INFORMATION

Fuels are generally not pure substances. They are mixtures with compositions that can vary. To simplify the analysis, we model or represent each of the fuels with a pure substance.

There are many different kinds of wood, each with a different density, fuel value, and economic value. But all are primarily composed of cellulose, which is a polymer of the sugar glucose, so we use glucose as a model for wood. Glucose has the chemical formula $C_6H_{12}O_6$, and polymerizes in a condensation reaction to produce cellulose. Use the standard enthalpies of formation of glucose, carbon dioxide, and water to estimate the enthalpy of combustion of wood. The average density of wood is about 0.5 g/mL.

Coal also is very complex and has a wide range of parameters relevant to an energy analysis. It is a brown or black sedimentary rock composed primarily of carbon and various amounts of other elements such as hydrogen, oxygen, sulfur, and nitrogen. The mass percent of carbon can range from 60% in a soft coal like lignite to greater than 90% in a hard coal like anthracite. The following mass percent composition data (C 85.0%, O 7.6%, H 5.0%, S 1.7%, and N 0.7%) is used to derive the empirical formula for our model compound ($C_{135}H_{96}O_9NS$, 1906 g/mol). Values for the enthalpy of combustion and density that are characteristic of coal are – 44,000 kJ/mol and 1.4 g/mL, respectively.

Heating oil, obtained by distilling petroleum, is similar to the diesel fuel that is burned in trucks and automobiles. It consists of a mixture of hydrocarbons having 14 to 20 carbon atoms with an average molar mass consistent with $C_{16}H_{34}$, which therefore is used as our model. Heating oil has a density of 0.80 g/mL and an enthalpy of combustion of –10,800 kJ/mol.

Liquefied petroleum gas (LPG) is a mixture of propane and butane. It mostly consists of propane, C_3H_8, which therefore is used as our model. LPG is extracted and purified from gas streams associated with oil and gas wells. It is a gas at room temperature and pressure but is stored and distributed as a liquid at pressures of approximately 10 atm (150 psi). Use the standard enthalpies of formation of propane, carbon dioxide, and water to estimate the enthalpy of combustion of LPG. The density of propane is 0.50 g/mL.

The cost of these fuels can vary significantly, depending on supply, demand, season, location, and amount purchased. For wood and coal, the cost also depends on the type purchased. A reasonable price for a cord of wood for use in heating is approximately $100. A cord is a stack which is 4 × 4 × 8 feet, weighing approximately 5000 pounds. A reasonable price for a ton of coal (2000 lbs) is approximately $80. The New York State Energy Research and Development Authority (www.nyserda.org), reports that the average price in New York State for both heating oil and LPG is $2.40/gal (effective May 31, 2009).

THE PROBLEM

Use the information from the Information section to complete Table 1, which summarizes properties of common fuels used for heating.

Use the information that you enter in Table 1 to determine the energy value, energy density, economic value, and environmental value of these fuels. Enter your results in Table 2.

Based on your calculations, identify which fuel has the largest and which has the smallest (1) energy value, (2) energy density, (3) economic value, and (4) environmental value.

Table 1 Properties of Common Fuels Used for Heating

Substance	Model Compound	Molar Mass g/mol	$\Delta H^{\circ}_{combustion}$ kJ/mol	Density g/mL	Cost
Wood	$C_6H_{12}O_6$				
Coal	$C_{135}H_{96}O_9NS$				
Heating Oil	$C_{16}H_{34}$				
LPG	C_3H_6				

Table 2 Quality of Common Fuels Used for Heating

Substance	Model Compound	Fuel Value kJ/g	Energy Density kJ/mL	Economic Value MJ/$	Environmental Value kJ/CO$_2$
Wood	$C_6H_{12}O_6$				
Coal	$C_{135}H_{96}O_9NS$				
Heating Oil	$C_{16}H_{34}$				
LPG	C_3H_8				

Lignite
Photo by Luis Miguel Bugallo Sánchez

Anthracite
Source: U.S. Geological Survey

SOLVE THE PROBLEM AND DOCUMENT YOUR SOLUTION

Name: _____

Other Team Members: _____

Date: _____   Activity Title: _____

Level of Help used to solve this problem by the team: *none* ☐   *Au* ☐   *Ag* ☐   *Cu* ☐

Work with your team to solve the problem. Your instructor can provide three levels of help called gold, silver, and copper. *Au Help* presents a strategy that resembles the way experts think when they solve problems. The use of this strategy is illustrated and prompted to different degrees in *Ag Help* and *Cu Help*. As the semester progresses, you should move through these stages of *Help* to grow your problem solving skills. Your instructor will tell you what you need to do to document your solution. One method would be to provide the information requested in *Au Help*.

❓ DOES YOUR ANSWER MAKE SENSE?

1. All of these fuels are used for heating. You should therefore expect that their figures of merit should be similar and not differ by more than a factor of 10. Do your calculated values for each of the four merit criteria lie within a factor of 10 of one another? If not, you should double check to make sure your calculations are correct.

2. You have probably heard that about half of the electrical power in the United States is generated by coal, which implies that coal is cheap and abundant. Do your calculations confirm that the economic value of coal is high?

3. You have probably heard that burning coal produces large quantities of greenhouse gases that contribute to climate change. Do your calculations in fact show that coal has a low environmental value?

▪ BUILDING YOUR PROBLEM-SOLVING SKILLS

You will be able to complete the *Got It!* section, which comes next, more efficiently, and you will do better on exams if you take a few minutes now to improve your problem-solving skills. Communicating the steps in your problem solution to others and thinking back on the problem that you just completed will help you to improve.

1. Share your team's problem solution with your class as called upon by the instructor.

2. Identify the most important thing you learned today about either the problem-solving process or a problem-solving skill that will help you solve new problems.

3. Consider whether you could solve this problem using a more efficient procedure so you can answer a similar exam question more quickly. If you find one, describe this more efficient procedure.

4. Identify whether there are any issues or assumptions contained in the problem and its solution that would limit using the same procedure for other problems.

5. Identify features of this problem and its solution that could apply to other problems.

1. Natural gas is extracted and purified from gas streams associated with oil and gas wells. It consists primarily of methane, CH_4. Because methane liquifies only at very low temperatures and high pressures, it is normally distributed through gas lines across the country that terminate at homes and businesses. The New York State Energy Research and Development Authority (www.nyserda.org), reports that the average price in New York State for natural gas is $14.69/1000 cubic feet (effective May 31, 2009). Even though the amount of gas used is measured volumetrically and therefore depends on the pressure and temperature of the gas, variations in the temperature and pressure appear not to be of concern to either the sellers or the buyers of natural gas. Therefore, in your calculations assume that standard thermodynamic conditions apply (1 atm pressure, 298 K). Use what you have learned in this activity to estimate the fuel value, energy density, economic value, and environmental value of natural gas. In your calculations, use standard enthalpies of formation to estimate the enthalpy of combustion, and use the ideal gas law to estimate the density of methane. For each of the four merit criteria, identify whether methane ranks higher or lower than any of the other fuels analyzed in this activity.

2. Here is a fun game, called **Battle of the Thermal Packs**. Your task is to design a hot pack and a cold pack that will exactly balance each other when placed in an insulated box. *Exactly balance* means that at the end, when equilibrium is established, the temperature inside the box will not have changed because the amount of energy released by the hot pack has been absorbed by the cold pack. The thermal packs must be based on the following chemical reactions:

$$CaCl_2(s) + H_2O(l) \rightarrow Ca^{2+}(aq) + 2Cl^-(aq) \qquad \Delta H°_{solvation} = -82 \text{ kJ/mol}$$

$$NH_4NO_3(s) + H_2O(l) \rightarrow NH_4^+(aq) + NO_3^-(aq) \qquad \Delta H°_{solvation} = +21 \text{ kJ/mol}$$

(handwritten annotations: "hot" above the -82 value; "cold" above the $+21$ value)

The thermochemical expressions for these reactions give you the balanced reaction equation for the salt dissolving in water along with the corresponding value of the standard enthalpy change for the reaction. To design your thermal packs, you need to specify the mass of salt and the mass of water that you will use in each pack, and identify which salt goes in the hot pack and which in the cold pack. The cold pack must contain enough salt, and no excess, to cool a 500 mL soft drink (density = 1.0 g/mL, specific heat = 4.5 J g^{-1} K^{-1}) and its glass bottle (heat capacity = 120 J K^{-1}) from 25 °C to 5 °C, and each thermal pack must weigh exactly 1 lb (454 g).

Solving Real Problems with Chemistry

ACTIVITY 7

IONIZING WITH LIGHT

Electrons can be removed from substances by exposing the substance to light. This effect is called the photoelectric effect, and the process is called photoionization. Albert Einstein received the Nobel Prize in 1921 for explaining how it occurs.

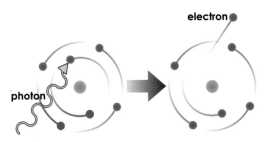

Figure 1 The Photoionization Process

Photoionization is observed when the light has sufficient energy to remove an electron, and the electron can escape from the surface of the substance without colliding with air molecules. Some light detectors, gas detectors, night vision goggles, and surveillance cameras that work at night utilize the photoelectric effect. Television video cameras used up until the late 1980s were also based on the photoelectric effect. Sunlight hitting the surface of spacecraft causes electrons to be emitted from the spacecraft into the surrounding vacuum, producing a charge on the spacecraft that can interfere with electronic instruments. Dust on the moon's surface can be ionized, and the electrostatic repulsion of the dust particles, because of their positive charge, causes the dust to rise from the surface.

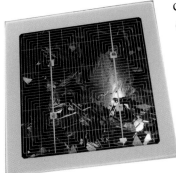

Solar or Photovoltaic Cell
(Wikimedia "Solar cell")

Modern television cameras, solar cells, and digital cameras take advantage of a variation of the photoelectric effect. In these devices, electrons are not ejected from the material but are excited from a non-conducting state to a conducting state in order to produce an electrical current.

Photoionization also occurs with atoms and molecules in the gas phase. Electron ionization energies of atoms and molecules can be measured in this way. This technique is called photoelectron spectroscopy (PES). PES is an important technique that is used in the analysis of materials to determine their composition (e.g., in forensic science) and in studies of new materials being developed for use as catalysts or in semiconductors. New and better catalysts are sought, for example, to reduce the costs of producing fuels and pharmaceutical products. New and better semiconductors are sought to reduce the size and increase the speed and versatility of many consumer products like cell phones, digital cameras, and computers.

Photoionization Gas Detectors
image provided by Baseline®-MOCON
www.pidsensor.com

✔ PREREQUISITE KNOWLEDGE

Before beginning this activity, you should be able to

- Convert between the wavelength, frequency, and energy of a photon

Contributed by John Goodwin, Coastal Carolina University
Revised by David Hanson, Stony Brook University

Upon completing this activity, you should be able to

- Identify a suitable material for a particular application of the photoelectric effect

- Predict approximate photoelectron spectra for a given atom

THE PROBLEM

A phototube, shown in Figure 2, has a photocathode (metal surface inside the tube) made of sodium metal. Light incident on the sodium causes electrons to be emitted. The electrons are collected by the positive electrode, producing a current in the external circuit. The current is measured while light of varying wavelengths and intensities is directed onto the photocathode. The electron kinetic energy can also be determined by varying the voltage on the positive electrode. The resulting data are shown in Table 1.

Your task is to use the data in Table 1 to:

1. Identify the relationship between the magnitude of the photocurrent and the light intensity and photon energy.

2. Identify the relationship between the energy of the emitted electrons and the light intensity and photon energy.

3. Express the relationships that you find in terms of graphs and mathematical equations.

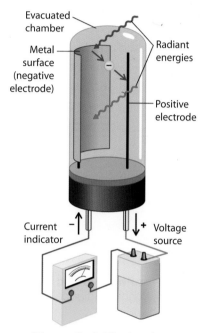

Figure 2 A Phototube

Scientist who work with the photoelectric effect use the units of electron volts (eV) for energy because then scientific notation with large negative exponents is not required. The relevant equality statement is $1 \text{ J} = 6.242 \times 10^{18}$ eV. You can see from this equality statement that 1 J is very large compared to an electron volt, so electron volts are more convenient units to use at the atomic level, while joules are more convenient at the macroscopic level.

Table 1 Photoelectric Effect Data

Wavelength, in nm	Relative Light Intensity	Photocurrent in microamps	Photon Energy in eV	Electron Kinetic Energy in eV
560	50	0		no electrons emitted
560	100	0		no electrons emitted
530	50	100		0.059
530	100	200		0.059
500	50	100		0.200
500	100	200		0.200

SOLVE THE PROBLEM AND DOCUMENT YOUR SOLUTION

Name: _____

Other Team Members: _____

Date: _____ Activity Title: _____

Level of Help used to solve this problem by the team: *none* ☐   *Au* ☐   *Ag* ☐   *Cu* ☐

Work with your team to solve the problem. Your instructor can provide three levels of help called gold, silver, and copper. *Au Help* presents a strategy that resembles the way experts think when they solve problems. The use of this strategy is illustrated and prompted to different degrees in *Ag Help* and *Cu Help*. As the semester progresses, you should move through these stages of *Help* to grow your problem solving skills. Your instructor will tell you what you need to do to document your solution. One method would be to provide the information requested in *Au Help*.

? DOES YOUR ANSWER MAKE SENSE?

1. Energy is delivered by light in packets called photons. The energy of each photon, E_p, is proportional to the frequency, v, of the light: $E_p = hv$. Does your analysis of the data in Table 1 support this idea? If so, describe how. If your analysis does not support the idea, explain why not.

2. The number of photons hitting the metal surface per second is related to the light intensity. As the number of photons increases, the number of electrons that are emitted increases, and the photocurrent increases. Does your analysis of the data in Table 1 support this idea? If so, describe how. If your analysis does not support the idea, explain why not.

3. It requires energy to remove electrons from atoms, molecules, and metals. This energy is called the binding energy or ionization energy. Does your analysis of the data in Table 1 support this idea? If so, describe how. If your analysis does not support the idea, explain why not.

■ BUILDING YOUR PROBLEM-SOLVING SKILLS

You will be able to complete the *Got It!* section, which comes next, more efficiently, and you will do better on exams if you take a few minutes now to improve your problem-solving skills. Communicating the steps in your problem solution to others and thinking back on the problem that you just completed will help you to improve.

1. Share your team's problem solution with your class as called upon by the instructor.

2. Identify the most important thing you learned about problem solving today that will help you solve new problems.

3. Consider whether you could solve this problem using a more efficient procedure so you can answer a similar exam question more quickly. If you find one, describe this more efficient procedure.

4. Identify whether there are any issues or assumptions contained in the problem and its solution that would limit using the same procedure for other problems.

5. Identify features of this problem and its solution that could apply to other problems.

1. Identify the metal in Table 2 that can be used to detect green light (540 nm) and produce electrons that have a kinetic energy of 0.2 eV. Justify your answer as being correct in terms of what you have learned in this activity.

Table 2   Work Functions of Some Metals

Metal	Work Function (eV)
Cesium	2.1
Potassium	2.3
Magnesium	3.7
Silver	4.3
Chromium	4.6
Nickel	5.2
Gold	5.4

2. Table 3 gives the ionization energies for the first 20 elements. These data were obtained from photoelectron spectra produced by ionizing with 1000 eV x-ray photons at the National Synchrotron Light Source at Brookhaven National Laboratory in Upton, New York. A photoelectron spectrum plots the photocurrent on the y-axis and the electron kinetic energy on the x-axis. Peaks occur where the photocurrent goes through maxima.

Table 3 Ionization Energies of Some Elements in Units 10^{-18} J

Element	1s	2s	2p	3s	3p	4s
H	2.18					
He	3.94					
Li	10.4	0.95				
Be	19.1	1.50				
B	32.1	2.26	1.32			
C	47.5	2.96	1.81			
N	65.8	4.04	2.32			
O	87.4	5.19	2.18			
F	112.0	6.45	2.79			
Ne	140.0	7.78	3.46			
Na	173.0	11.4	6.10	0.83		
Mg	209.0	15.1	8.83	1.23		
Al	251.0	20.1	13.0	1.81	0.96	
Si	296.0	25.1	17.1	2.43	1.31	
P	346.0	31.1	22.4	3.24	1.68	
S	397.0	37.7	27.4	3.41	1.66	
Cl	454.0	44.6	33.6	4.06	2.08	
Ar	514.0	52.4	40.1	4.69	2.53	
K	577.0	61.7	48.4	6.53	3.96	0.70
Ca	648.0	71.0	56.5	7.73	4.82	0.98

a. What is the equation that describes the relationship between the photon energy, the electron ionization energy, and the electron kinetic energy?

b. Use the data in Table 3 to show what the photoelectron spectrum for fluorine looks like. Put the electron kinetic energy scale on the x-axis and draw lines at the energies where the photocurrent goes through maxima when the photon energy is 1.60×10^{-16} J.

c. Explain how the data in Table 3 provides evidence that electrons in atoms are organized in shells and subshells with different binding energies.

ACTIVITY 8

ORIGIN OF COLOR-BLINDNESS

Our senses of taste, smell, sight, hearing, and touch depend upon elegant biological machinery that can transform chemical and physical stimuli into neural information interpreted by our brains. Our ability to see different colors depends on the presence of three photoreceptor proteins called *photopsins* that are located in the cone cells of the retina. Each of these photoreceptor molecules has a characteristic sensitivity to light of certain wavelengths.

The rod cells in the retina contain a similar protein called *rhodopsin* (also called visual purple and designated R) that does not function in bright light but is highly sensitive to dim light and thereby provides night vision.

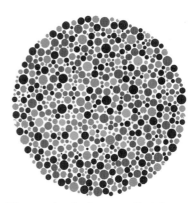

Figure 1 A diagram that has a red-shaded number 42 embedded in it tests for color-blindness.

The brain perceives colors by sensing and combining the response from each of the three photopsins, which are designated L, M, and S. Only the L receptor responds strongly to red light so the brain recognizes that signal as red. Only the S receptor responds strongly to violet light so the brain recognizes that signal as violet. Colors between red and violet stimulate more than one receptor, and the brain interprets the relative signal levels from the different receptors in terms of different colors. For example, yellowish-green light stimulates L and M receptors equally strongly and stimulates S-receptors weakly. Blue-green light stimulates M and S receptors more strongly than L receptors.

A deviation from the normal sensitivity or functionality of one or more photopsins produces color blindness.

✔ PREREQUISITE KNOWLEDGE

Before beginning this activity, you should be able to

- Associate colors with different wavelengths of light

- Inter-relate the wavelength and frequency of light

- Calculate the energy of a photon given the frequency of the light

- Explain the origin of absorption and emission line spectra of atoms

Contributed by John Goodwin, Coastal Carolina University
Revised by David Hanson, Stony Brook University

APPLYING YOUR NEW SKILLS

Upon completing this activity, you should be able to

- Identify the reason for the loss of color vision in dim light in terms of the absorption spectra of the different photopsins

- Analyze absorption spectra of an acid-base indicator to identify its color in acidic and basic solutions

THE PROBLEM

The absorption spectra of the three photopsins and rhodopsin are shown in Figure 2. A common form of color-blindness is called *deuteranomoly*, which is characterized by the inability to distinguish between green and red. Your task is to explain how a mutation shifting the absorbance of one of the photopsins to the red or blue could cause deuteranomoly.

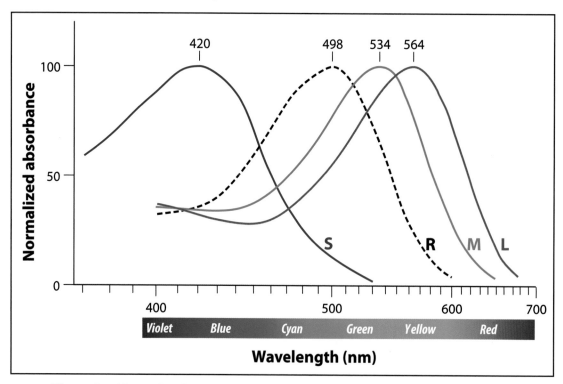

Figure 2 Absorption Spectra of Rhodopsin (R), Photopsin III (S), Photopsin II (M), and Photopsin I (L). Adapted from Wikipedia/Photopsin.

Approximate wavelength ranges for the colors are given at right:

Color	Wavelength
Violet	390 – 425 nm
Blue	425 – 475 nm
Green	475 – 550 nm
Yellow	550 – 590 nm
Red	590 – 690 nm

✓ SOLVE THE PROBLEM AND DOCUMENT YOUR SOLUTION

Name: _____

Other Team Members: _____

Date: _____   Activity Title: _____

Level of Help used to solve this problem by the team: *none* ☐   *Au* ☐   *Ag* ☐   *Cu* ☐

Work with your team to solve the problem. Your instructor can provide three levels of help called gold, silver, and copper. *Au Help* presents a strategy that resembles the way experts think when they solve problems. The use of this strategy is illustrated and prompted to different degrees in *Ag Help* and *Cu Help*. As the semester progresses, you should move through these stages of *Help* to grow your problem solving skills. Your instructor will tell you what you need to do to document your solution. One method would be to provide the information requested in *Au Help*.

? DOES YOUR ANSWER MAKE SENSE?

1. How is your answer consistent with the fact that different opsins absorb different wavelengths of light?

2. How is your answer consistent with the fact that the response of three opsins is necessary for color vision?

BUILDING YOUR PROBLEM-SOLVING SKILLS

You will be able to complete the *Got It!* section, which comes next, more efficiently, and you will do better on exams if you take a few minutes now to improve your problem-solving skills. Communicating the steps in your problem solution to others and thinking back on the problem that you just completed will help you to improve.

1. Share your team's problem solution with your class as called upon by the instructor.

2. Identify the most important thing you learned about problem solving today that will help you solve new problems.

3. Consider whether you could solve this problem using a more efficient procedure so you can answer a similar exam question more quickly. If you find one, describe this more efficient procedure.

4. Identify whether there are any issues or assumptions contained in the problem and its solution that would limit using the same procedure for other problems.

5. Identify features of this problem and its solution that could apply to other problems.

![GOT IT!](lightbulb icon) **GOT IT!**

1. In terms of the absorption spectra of the opsins and their activity in bright and dim light, explain why the bright yellow petals of a flower might be expected to appear dark and colorless compared to green leaves, in the very dim light of evening.

2. Absorption spectra of an acid-base indictor are shown in Figure 3. An acid-base indictor loses an H^+ ion in basic solution and the absorption spectrum shifts. Consequently, the indicator is one color in an acidic solution and yet another color in a basic solution. Use what you have learned in this activity to predict the color of the acidic solution and the color of the basic solution for this indicator. Provide a rationale for your answer.

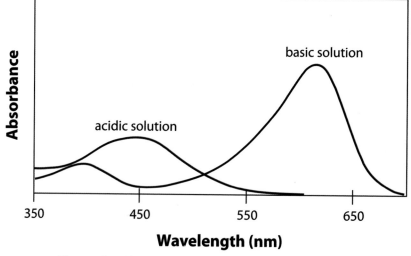

Figure 3   Absorption Spectra of the Acid Form and the Base Form of an Acid-Base Indicator

REACTIVE MOLECULES

In addition to large biomolecules like proteins, nucleic acids, lipids, and carbohydrates, many small inorganic molecules and ions are involved in life processes. For example, molecular oxygen, O_2, is essential in the metabolism of glucose (sugar), and carbon dioxide, CO_2, is a product. Carbon dioxide also generates carbonic acid and bicarbonate and carbonate ions in the blood; nitric oxide, NO, is known to be a neurotransmitter and vasodilator; and common ions like hydroxide, OH^-, and hydronium, H_3O^+, are ubiquitous. Considering that complex mixtures of small molecules occur, can you use your knowledge of chemical structure to predict which molecules are relatively unreactive and stable and which are not?

✔ PREREQUISITE KNOWLEDGE

Before beginning this activity, you should be able to

- Convert a chemical formula into a Lewis structure, including resonance structures as needed

- Determine bond orders and formal charges in Lewis structures

- Recognize features that increase the stability of a molecule: resonance structures and bond orders greater than 1

- Recognize features that decrease the stability of a molecule: unpaired electrons, formal charges that represent charge separation, and unusual oxidation numbers

- Use inorganic nomenclature to determine molecular formulas

Contributed by John Goodwin (v10), Coastal Carolina University

◎ APPLYING YOUR NEW SKILLS

Upon completing this activity, you should be able to

- Use Lewis structures to predict the relative reactivity of similar chemical species given their chemical formulas

- Use Lewis structures to explain whether a given reaction is likely or not likely to occur

🧩 THE PROBLEM

For each molecule in the pairs given below,

1. Draw the Lewis structure, including formal charges and resonance structures, if any

2. Determine the bond orders

3. Determine the oxidation numbers of the atoms

4. Identify when one of the molecules has an unpaired electron+

Use this information to predict which molecule of the pair is the more reactive and justify your choice.

O_2 and O_2^- NO_2 and NO_2^- H_2O and H_2O_2

NO_3^- and $ONOO^-$ O_2 and O_3

Name: _____

Other Team Members: _____

Date: _____ Activity Title: _____

Level of Help used to solve this problem by the team: *none* ☐ *Au* ☐ *Ag* ☐ *Cu* ☐

Work with your team to solve the problem. Your instructor can provide three levels of help called gold, silver, and copper. *Au Help* presents a strategy that resembles the way experts think when they solve problems. The use of this strategy is illustrated and prompted to different degrees in *Ag Help* and *Cu Help*. As the semester progresses, you should move through these stages of *Help* to grow your problem solving skills. Your instructor will tell you what you need to do to document your solution. One method would be to provide the information requested in *Au Help*.

? DOES YOUR ANSWER MAKE SENSE?

1. Were you able to justify your identification of the more reactive species in each pair? Summarize the principles that you used below.

BUILDING YOUR PROBLEM-SOLVING SKILLS

You will be able to complete the *Got It!* section, which comes next, more efficiently, and you will do better on exams if you take a few minutes now to improve your problem-solving skills. Communicating the steps in your problem solution to others and thinking back on the problem that you just completed will help you to improve.

1. Share your team's problem solution with your class as called upon by the instructor.

2. Identify the most important thing you learned today about either the problem-solving process or a problem-solving skill that will help you solve new problems.

3. Consider whether you could solve this problem using a more efficient procedure so you can answer a similar exam question more quickly. If you find one, describe this more efficient procedure.

4. Identify whether there are any issues or assumptions contained in the problem and its solution that would limit using the same procedure for other problems.

5. Identify features of this problem and its solution that could apply to other problems.

 **GOT IT!**

1. Which molecule in the following pairs do you predict will be the more reactive? Explain why for each case.

   a. chlorine dioxide, ClO_2, or the chlorite ion, ClO_2^-

   b. the nitrogen molecule, N_2, or hydrazine, N_2H_4

c. carbon monoxide or carbon dioxide

2. The formation of the peroxynitrite ion, written as ONOO⁻, in living organisms has been ascribed to the reaction between nitric oxide, NO, and superoxide, O_2^-.

a. Write a chemical reaction equation for the formation of peroxynitrite.

b. Draw Lewis structures of the reactants and product.

c. Suggest why peroxynitrite forms from NO and O_2^-.

3. The following species are isoelectronic, i.e., they all have the same number of electons. Draw their Lewis stuctures and explain in terms of the Lewis structures which are stable and which do not exist.

$$CO_3^{2-} \qquad NO_3^- \qquad O_4 \qquad SO_3$$

Solving Real Problems with Chemistry

VITAMINS C AND E: WHERE DO THOSE VITAMINS GO?

Dietary supplements such as vitamins are taken by 52% of the American adult population and have become a multi-billion dollar industry.[1] Vitamins are small molecules that are essential for our health. We obtain most of the vitamins that we need from food because they are not synthesized in our bodies.

Vitamins are divided into two categories: those that are water soluble (hydrophilic) and those that are not water soluble (hydrophobic). Hydrophilic vitamins dissolve in the blood. Hydrophobic vitamins do not dissolve in the blood directly; rather, they are transported by blood lipoproteins and absorbed by fatty membranes and tissues.

You may have heard some people advocating mega doses of vitamins to improve your health, but large doses of hydrophobic vitamins can have a harmful effect because they are stored with fat in cells and dissolve in fatty tissue. As a result, concentrations in the tissues build up over time and a high concentration is maintained in the bloodstream. Hydrophilic vitamins, on the other hand, are not soluble in fatty tissue. They remain dissolved in the blood and are eliminated quite rapidly through the kidneys. Consequently high concentrations of hydrophilic vitamins are not maintained in the body.

Vitamins C and E are among the most popular vitamins, so it is a good idea to know more about them. This activity will help you understand how the molecular structure of vitamins C and E affects their solubility. You will also explore the relationship between dosage and solubility.

Vitamin C is an antioxidant and a coenzyme. As an antioxidant, it neutralizes reactive molecules (free radicals) in cells, reduces damage to cells, and even may reduce the risk of cancer. As a coenzyme, it contributes to the enzymatic synthesis of essential molecules such as collagen, which is the main connective protein in joints.

Vitamin E is actually a group of 8 isomers with structures similar to the one shown in Figure 1. A number of studies indicate that vitamin E, which functions as a powerful antioxidant, may prevent heart disease, cancer, cataracts, Alzheimer's disease, and age-related macular degeneration.

Figure 1 The Structures of Vitamins C and E

Vitamin C
(ascorbic acid)

Vitamin E

Contributed by Renee Cole, University of Central Missouri,
Linda Hobart, Finger Lakes Community College, and
Fred Yost, Carteret Community College
Revised by Rong Chen, Debra Rust, and David Hanson, Stony Brook University

✔ PREREQUISITE KNOWLEDGE

Before beginning this activity, you should be able to

- List the types of intermolecular interactions important for any molecule given the structure of that molecule
- Identify a molecule as hydrophobic or hydrophilic based on its structure
- Determine the half-life of a substance from a graph of concentration versus time

◎ APPLYING YOUR NEW SKILLS

After completing this activity, you should be able to

- Use your knowledge of molecular structure to predict relative rates of retention of different substances in the bloodstream
- Recommend dosing schedules based on molecular structure and half-life

🧩 THE PROBLEM

After reading about the risks and benefits of taking vitamin supplements as part of your daily routine, you decide to start taking vitamins C and E to decrease your risk of heart attack and cancer. Some articles recommend taking mega doses more than once a day, while others suggest you take the Recommended Daily Allowance (RDA).

The dose of a medication must be high enough to maintain the therapeutic effect but not so high that it causes side effects. When a drug is given, it reaches its peak concentration (C_{max}) in the blood pretty quickly. The concentration then decreases as the drug is broken down or removed from the blood. The lowest concentration, just before the next dose, is referred to as C_{min} or the trough level. The half-life of the medication must be long enough to allow for a reasonable dose schedule. Many products are being developed with a half-life long enough for them to be taken only once each day.

Figures 2 and 3 show the concentrations of vitamins C and E in the blood as a function of time after the initial dosage. Note the scale difference of the x-axes.

You have to use your knowledge of solubility to determine which figure is for vitamin C and which is for vitamin E.

What dosage and frequency would you suggest, considering the structures and solubility properties of these two different vitamins?

Figure 2

Time (min)	Blood Level of X (µmol/L)
0	34
2	205
3	456
4	806
10	702
20	530
30	420
40	346
50	264
60	210
70	174
80	130
90	99
100	85

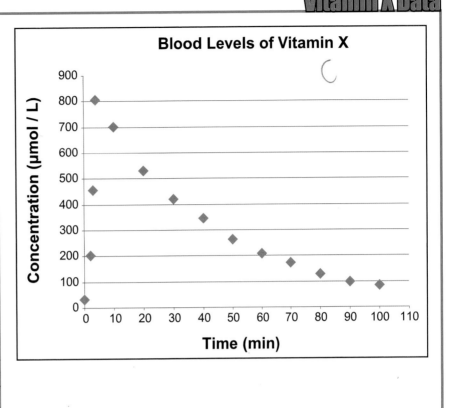

Figure 3

Time (hours)	Blood Level of Y (µmol/L)
0	0.2
5	0.6
10	2.1
20	1.8
40	1.1
80	0.6
120	0.3

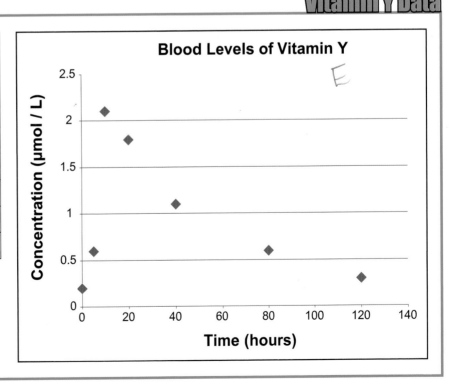

Activity 10 — *Vitamins C and E: Where Do Those Vitamins Go?*

Name: _____

Other Team Members: _____

Date: _____ Activity Title: _____

Level of Help used to solve this problem by the team: *none* ☐   *Au* ☐   *Ag* ☐   *Cu* ☐

Work with your team to solve the problem. Your instructor can provide three levels of help called gold, silver, and copper. *Au Help* presents a strategy that resembles the way experts think when they solve problems. The use of this strategy is illustrated and prompted to different degrees in *Ag Help* and *Cu Help*. As the semester progresses, you should move through these stages of *Help* to grow your problem solving skills. Your instructor will tell you what you need to do to document your solution. One method would be to provide the information requested in *Au Help*.

1. Do the dosage and frequency you suggest agree with common sense (i.e., are they much longer or shorter than the time scales in Figures 2 and 3)? Explain why those time scales are relevant.

2. Do the dosage and frequency you suggest agree with the properties you deduced from the molecular structures? Explain.

BUILDING YOUR PROBLEM-SOLVING SKILLS

You will be able to complete the *Got It!* section, which comes next, more efficiently, and you will do better on exams if you take a few minutes now to improve your problem-solving skills. Communicating the steps in your problem solution to others and thinking back on the problem that you just completed will help you to improve.

1. Share your team's problem solution with your class as called upon by the instructor.

2. Identify the most important thing you learned about problem solving today that will help you solve new problems.

3. Consider whether you could solve this problem using a more efficient procedure so you can answer a similar exam question more quickly. If you find one, describe this more efficient procedure.

4. Identify whether there are any issues or assumptions contained in the problem and its solution that would limit using the same procedure for other problems.

5. Identify features of this problem and its solution that could apply to other problems.

1. Predict which of the vitamins shown at right would be retained longer in the bloodstream. Explain.

Vitamin B3
(niacin)

Vitamin D3
(cholecalciferol)

2. Amoxicillin and azithromicin are common antibiotics. Amoxicillin usually is taken every 6 hours for 10 days, while azithromicin is taken once a day for 5 days. Based on these regimens, what can you predict about their half-lives and molecular structures? Explain your predictions. Look up the structures of these antibiotics and half-lives in the body to validate your predictions. Account for any differences.

REFERENCES

[1]American Journal of Epidemiology, see http://aje.oxforjournals.org/cgi/content/full/160/4/339

DESIGNING A FUEL INJECTOR FOR THE DODGE VIPER

Behold the Dodge Viper:
The 2008 version of its engine produces *600* horsepower!

To maximize the power of the engine and minimize the concentrations of pollutants in exhaust gases, the proportion of gasoline to air in the cylinders during combustion must be balanced. In this activity, you will calculate the maximum quantity of gasoline that can be injected into one of the cylinders of the Viper engine and burn completely.

The Viper is powered by an 8.40 L V-10 engine. The "V" refers to the orientation of the cylinders in engine block shown on the right. There are two banks of 5 cylinders each (under the two red covers in the photo) that form a "V" if viewed from the end of the engine. The 8.40 L refers to the total combustion volume of this engine. There are 10 cylinders, so the volume inside each cylinder must be 8.40 L ÷ 10 = 0.840 L. The diagram of a single cylinder is shown below.

Pentroof Hemi Engine Design

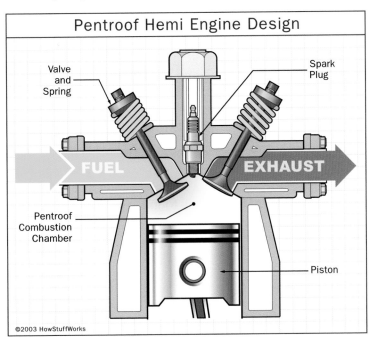

Valve and Spring

Spark Plug

FUEL

EXHAUST

Pentroof Combustion Chamber

Piston

©2003 HowStuffWorks

Reprinted courtesy of HowStuffWorks.com

Combustion occurs in the gas phase even when the fuel is a liquid or solid. For example, the flames produced by logs burning in a fireplace result from the combustion of the flammable gases released by logs at the high temperature of the fire. In automobile engines, liquid gasoline is injected into the engine in such a way that it is quickly vaporized prior to combustion.

Contributed by Tom Gilbert, Northeastern University

✔ PREREQUISITE KNOWLEDGE

Before beginning this activity, you should be able to

- Convert between masses and moles and between the mass and volume of a substance

- Write and balance chemical reaction equations

- Determine the amounts of reactants that react and the amounts of products that are produced in a chemical reaction

- Use the ideal gas law to relate the pressure, volume, temperature, and number of moles of a gas

- Use Dalton's law of partial pressures to relate the total pressure, partial pressures, and composition of a gas mixture

◎ APPLYING YOUR NEW SKILLS

After completing this activity, you should be able to

- Correctly determine the quantity of a hydrocarbon fuel that can be mixed with air and burned completely under given conditions of atmospheric pressure, temperature, and volume

- Correctly determine the volume of a gas-phase reactant at a given temperature and pressure that reacts completely with a quantity of another reactant

THE PROBLEM

Your task is to determine the volume of liquid gasoline that would consume the oxygen (O_2) present in 0.840 L of air during complete combustion of the fuel.

INFORMATION

- Use pure iso-octane, C_8H_{18} as a model for the mixture of hydrocarbons found in gasoline, since that is the compound on which an octane rating is based

- The density of iso-octane is 0.70 g/mL

- Assume air enters the cylinder at a pressure of 1.00 atm

- Air is a mixture of gases; assume the mole fraction of O_2 in air is 21%

- Assume air behaves as an ideal gas, so the ideal gas law ($PV = nRT$) applies

- The temperature of the air is the operating temperature of the engine: 190 °F

68   Solving Real Problems with Chemistry

☑ SOLVE THE PROBLEM AND DOCUMENT YOUR SOLUTION

Name: _____

Other Team Members: _____

Date: _____ Activity Title: _____

Level of Help used to solve this problem by the team: *none* ☐ *Au* ☐ *Ag* ☐ *Cu* ☐

Work with your team to solve the problem. Your instructor can provide three levels of help called gold, silver, and copper. *Au Help* presents a strategy that resembles the way experts think when they solve problems. The use of this strategy is illustrated and prompted to different degrees in *Ag Help* and *Cu Help*. As the semester progresses, you should move through these stages of *Help* to grow your problem solving skills. Your instructor will tell you what you need to do to document your solution. One method would be to provide the information requested in *Au Help*.

? DOES YOUR ANSWER MAKE SENSE?

1. What are the units of the value you calculated? Are they units of volume? If your answer has a value less than one, what other units could you use to produce an answer that is greater than one?

2. How does the volume of liquid octane you calculated compare to the volume of air in the cylinder? Does the difference between the two volumes seem reasonable? Explain why or why not.

BUILDING YOUR PROBLEM-SOLVING SKILLS

You will be able to complete the *Got It!* section, which comes next, more efficiently, and you will do better on exams if you take a few minutes now to improve your problem-solving skills. Communicating the steps in your problem solution to others and thinking back on the problem that you just completed will help you to improve.

1. Share your team's problem solution with your class as called upon by the instructor.

2. Identify the most important thing you learned today about either the problem-solving process or a problem-solving skill that will help you solve new problems.

3. Consider whether you could solve this problem using a more efficient procedure so you can answer a similar exam question more quickly. If you find one, describe this more efficient procedure.

4. Identify whether there are any issues or assumptions contained in the problem and its solution that would limit using the same procedure for other problems.

5. Identify features of this problem and its solution that could apply to other problems.

1. A Volkswagen GTI has a 4 cylinder 1.8 L turbo-charged engine. If the turbo-charger produces an air pressure in the cylinder of 2.0 atm, what volume of gasoline must be injected into each cylinder during each cycle of the engine to react completely with the oxygen that is present in the air in one cylinder?

2. Automobile air bags inflate during a crash because of the rapid generation of nitrogen gas from the decomposition of sodium azide:

$$2 \, NaN_3(s) \rightarrow 2 \, Na(s) + 3 \, N_2(g)$$

How many grams of sodium azide are needed to fill a 50 cm × 50 cm × 25 cm air bag to a pressure of 1.20 atm at a temperature of 15 °C?

3. An acetylene-oxygen torch (C_2H_2/O_2) is often used for welding. What must the ratio of flow rates be for the acetylene and oxygen gases so they react completely with each other? The flow rate is measured in L/min. You should (a) identify any assumptions that you made in answering this question and (b) explain why you think your answer is correct in terms of the ideal gas law.

ACTIVITY 12

MINING METHANE HYDRATES: FIRE FROM ICE!

There are vast quantities of fossil hydrocarbons trapped at a low temperature and high pressure in cages of frozen water under sediment at the bottom of the oceans. The water cage in which methane, CH_4, is trapped is known as *methane hydrate*. With appropriate recovery technologies, these compounds, which are called *clathrates*, could be mined for use as fuel. The locations of methane hydrate reserves are shown on the map in Figure 1. Figure 2 shows a sample of methane gas burning as the clathrate melts. The inset is a model of the ice/methane crystal structure.

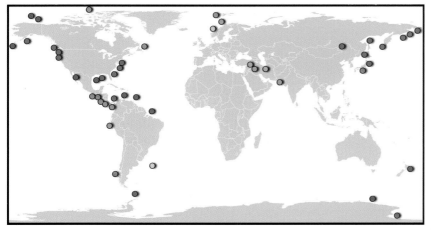

Figure 1   Map Showing the Location of Methane Hydrate Reserves

In this activity you will use the properties of methane hydrate, phase diagrams, and heating curves to answer questions about the conditions under which this compound exists and how it can be recovered in mining operations.

Figure 2   Clathrates, the Structure of Methane Hydrate, and Methane Burning as it is Released

✔ PREREQUISITE KNOWLEDGE

Before beginning this activity, you should be able to

- Convert between different units of pressure and temperature

- Describe the different parts of a phase diagram

- Relate heating curves to the relevant quantitative calorimetric and thermochemical information for heating a substance and causing a phase transition

Contributed by John Goodwin (v10), Coastal Carolina University   *© POGIL-IC Project*

APPLYING YOUR NEW SKILLS

After completing this activity, you should be able to

*   Identify regions of stable phases and the pressures and temperatures at which phase transitions occur on a phase diagram

*   Use phase diagrams to analyze strategies involving phase changes for storing and recovering materials under specified conditions of temperature and pressure

INFORMATION

Table 1   Properties of Methane Hydrate

Molecular formula	$(CH_4)_8(H_2O)_{46}$
Enthalpy of decomposition	54 kJ/mol
Specific heat capacity	2.1 J/g deg
Density	0.9 g/cm³

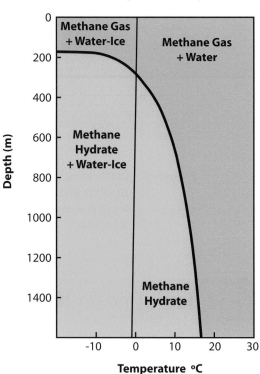

Figure 3   Methane Hydrate Phase Diagram, Ocean Depth vs. Temperature

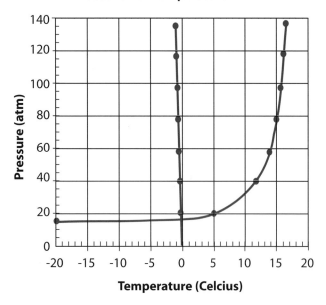

Figure 4   Methane Hydrate Phase Diagram, Pressure vs. Temperature

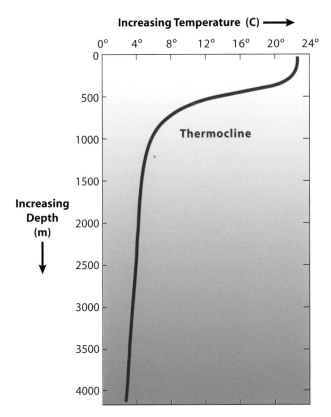

Figure 5 Variation in Ocean Water Temperature with Depth

Increasing Temperature (C) ⟶

0° 4° 8° 12° 16° 20° 24°

Increasing Depth (m)

Thermocline

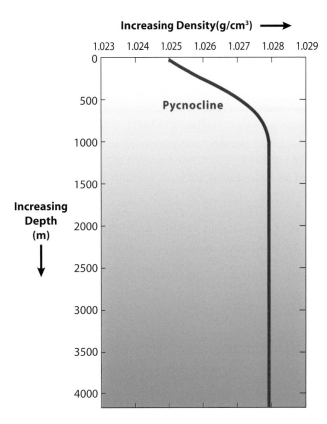

Figure 6 Variation in Ocean Water Density with Depth

Increasing Density(g/cm³) ⟶

1.023 1.024 1.025 1.026 1.027 1.028 1.029

Increasing Depth (m)

Pycnocline

THE PROBLEM

As a chemical engineer working with a mining company, your task is to answer and justify your answers to several questions posed by management about methane hydrate deposits reportedly found by a contract explorer for your company on the Blake Ridge at a depth of 1000 m off the shores of South Carolina. These questions are listed in the next section. Some helpful information is provided in the previous section.

The phase diagrams in Figures 3 and 4 show the values of water depth, pressure, and temperature under which solid methane hydrate can exist. The boundary lines correspond to points between phases. Figure 5 shows how the temperature of ocean water varies with depth, and Figure 6 shows how the density of ocean water varies with depth.

The enthalpy of combustion in Table 1 tells you how much energy is required to decompose 1 mole of methane hydrate into methane gas and water, and the specific heat capacity in Table 1 tells you how much energy is needed to heat 1 gram of methane hydrate by 1 °C.

Name: _____

Other Team Members: _____

Date: _____ Activity Title: _____

Level of Help used to solve this problem by the team: *none* ☐   *Au* ☐   *Ag* ☐   *Cu* ☐

Work with your team to solve the problem. Your instructor can provide three levels of help called gold, silver, and copper. *Au Help* presents a strategy that resembles the way experts think when they solve problems. The use of this strategy is illustrated and prompted to different degrees in *Ag Help* and *Cu Help*. As the semester progresses, you should move through these stages of *Help* to grow your problem solving skills. Your instructor will tell you what you need to do to document your solution. One method would be to provide the information requested in *Au Help*.

1. Is it reasonable to find methane hydrate at a depth of 1000 m (i.e., does a stable phase of methane hydrate exist at the temperature and pressure at that depth)? Explain your answer.

2. If we can dig the methane hydrate out from under the sediment, will it then lie on the bottom or will it float to the surface? Explain your answer.

3. If methane hydrate floats to the surface, can we harvest it as a solid from the surface or will it decompose on the way up, releasing all the methane gas before we can capture it? Explain your answer.

4. At what temperature will methane hydrate decompose at 1000 m and release the methane? Explain your answer.

5. How much energy is required to raise the temperature and decompose 1 kg of methane hydrate at a depth of 1000 m? Explain your answer.

6. How many moles of methane can be obtained from 1 kg of methane hydrate? Explain your answer.

7. How many liters of methane at 1 atm pressure and 300 K can be obtained from 1 kg of methane hydrate? Explain your answer.

? DOES YOUR ANSWER MAKE SENSE?

1. Does the stability of methane hydrate under the ocean floor seem reasonable given the conditions there? Explain.

2. Do your answers indicate that it is easy or technologically challenging to mine methane hydrate under the ocean floor? Explain.

BUILDING YOUR PROBLEM-SOLVING SKILLS

You will be able to complete the *Got It!* section, which comes next, more efficiently, and you will do better on exams if you take a few minutes now to improve your problem-solving skills. Communicating the steps in your problem solution to others and thinking back on the problem that you just completed will help you to improve.

1. Share your team's problem solution with your class as called upon by the instructor.

2. Identify the most important thing you learned about problem solving today that will help you solve new problems.

3. Consider whether you could solve this problem using a more efficient procedure so you can answer a similar exam question more quickly. If you find one, describe this more efficient procedure.

4. Identify whether there are any issues or assumptions contained in the problem and its solution that would limit using the same procedure for other problems.

5. Identify features of this problem and its solution that could apply to other problems.

1. If your mining company decided it would be more practical to remove the methane hydrate as a solid in a pressurized container, what pressure would need to be held by the container at 60 °F? Explain.

2. Hydrogen gas, H₂, would be an ideal fuel. It could be produced by decomposing water using solar energy, and the combustion product is water back again. One major barrier to the use of hydrogen in fuel cells for cars is safe storage and handling. Much research is presently going into finding materials that can trap H₂ in a solid form. One exciting prospect is the recent preparation of hydrogen hydrates (also called hydrogen clathrates) that are similar to the naturally occurring methane hydrates.

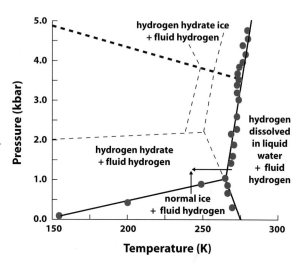

A phase diagram of a hydrogen hydrate using information from a recent research article is shown here. The article discusses the process indicated by the vertical arrow in the diagram.

   a. Describe the process indicated by the vertical arrow. In your description, identify the composition of the initial phase, the composition of the final phase, and the pressure in atmospheres and the temperature in Fahrenheit at which the phase transition occurs.

   b. If a storage system were designed to maintain the pressure indicated by the horizontal arrow, what change in temperature conditions would be necessary to release gas phase hydrogen by this system? Explain.

REFERENCES

http://www.netl.doe.gov/scngo/NaturalGas/hydrates/about-hydrates/conditions.htm

http://en.wikipedia.org/wiki/Methane_clathrate

Kvenvolden, K. A. 1998. A primer on the geological occurrence of gas hydrate. In: Henriet, J-P. & Mienert, J. (Eds) Gas Hydrates: Relevance to World Margin Stability and Climate Change. Geological Society, London, Special Publications, 1379-30.

Lokshin, Konstantin A.; Zhao, Yusheng. Fast synthesis method and phase diagram of hydrogen clathrate hydrate. Applied Physics Letters (2006), 88(13).

Solving Real Problems with Chemistry

ACTIVITY 13

THE SOURCE OF CELLULAR ENERGY: ATP REACTING WITH WATER

Many science students and most biology students know that much of the Gibbs free energy that drives reactions in our cells comes from the reaction of adenosine triphosphate, ATP, with water. The availability of Gibbs free energy to drive another reaction is identified by the negative ΔG value for this reaction. What is so special about ATP and its reaction with water? What is the origin of the free energy used to drive so many important reactions?

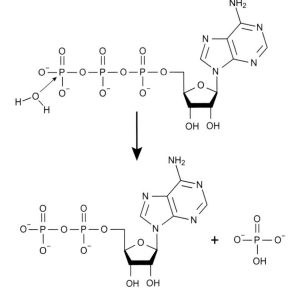

Figure 1   The Hydrolysis Reaction of ATP with Water

Figure 2   Stick Model of ATP Based on X-ray Diffraction Data

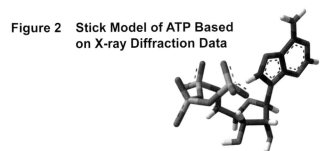

✔ PREREQUISITE KNOWLEDGE

Before beginning this activity, you should be able to

- Draw Lewis structures including resonance structures to predict the effect of changes in molecular structure on ΔH, ΔS, and ΔG

- Estimate the change in enthalpy, ΔH, for a chemical reaction from bond energies

- Identify whether the change in entropy, ΔS, for a chemical reaction is positive or negative

- Determine ΔG for a chemical reaction from ΔH and ΔS

◎ APPLYING YOUR NEW SKILLS

After completing this activity, you should be able to

- Analyze changes in molecular structure associated with the hydrolysis of ATP, ADP, and other phosphate-containing molecules to predict the effect on ΔH, ΔS, and ΔG

- Analyze changes in molecular structure associated with chemical reactions to predict the effect on ΔH, ΔS, and ΔG

Contributed by Vicky Minderhout, Seattle University, and David Hanson, Stony Brook University   © POGIL-IC Project

Your task is to explain the source of the large negative Gibbs free energy in terms of the changes in molecular structure when ATP reacts with water. Consider bond energies, resonance stabilization, and charge destabilization. This activity will give you insight into the reason that the hydrolysis reaction of ATP **releases** energy even though breaking an individual chemical bond *always* requires an **input** of energy—a positive value of ΔH.

Reported values for ΔH and ΔS are –24.3 kJ/mol and 21.6 J/mol K at body temperature of 37 °C.

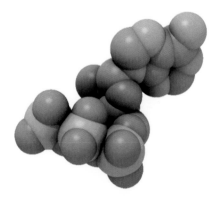

SOLVE THE PROBLEM AND DOCUMENT YOUR SOLUTION

Name: _____

Other Team Members: _____

Date: _____   Activity Title: _____

Level of Help used to solve this problem by the team: **none** ☐   *Au* ☐   *Ag* ☐   *Cu* ☐

Work with your team to solve the problem. Your instructor can provide three levels of help called gold, silver, and copper. *Au Help* presents a strategy that resembles the way experts think when they solve problems. The use of this strategy is illustrated and prompted to different degrees in *Ag Help* and *Cu Help.* As the semester progresses, you should move through these stages of *Help* to grow your problem solving skills. Your instructor will tell you what you need to do to document your solution. One method would be to provide the information requested in *Au Help.*

? DOES YOUR ANSWER MAKE SENSE?

1. Did you find that changes in the number and types of bonds contribute to the change in enthalpy? Explain.

2. Did you find that changes in resonance structures and charge distributions contribute to the change in enthalpy? Explain.

BUILDING YOUR PROBLEM-SOLVING SKILLS

You will be able to complete the *Got It!* section, which comes next, more efficiently, and you will do better on exams if you take a few minutes now to improve your problem-solving skills. Communicating the steps in your problem solution to others and thinking back on the problem that you just completed will help you to improve.

1. Share your team's problem solution with your class as called upon by the instructor.

2. Identify the most important thing you learned about problem solving today that will help you solve new problems.

3. Consider whether you could solve this problem using a more efficient procedure so you can answer a similar exam question more quickly. If you find one, describe this more efficient procedure.

4. Identify whether there are any issues or assumptions contained in the problem and its solution that would limit using the same procedure for other problems.

5. Identify features of this problem and its solution that could apply to other problems.

1. P_4O_{10} reacts with water to produce phosphoric acid. Using bond energies, estimate the change in enthalpy for this reaction and predict whether the change in entropy is positive or negative.

$$P_4O_{10}(s) + H_2O(l) \rightarrow H_3PO_4(s)$$

2. An amide linkage is important in biology, as it couples amino acids together to form proteins. Consider acetic acid reacting with methyl amine to produce N-methyl-acetamide. Estimate the change in enthalpy using bond energies, then predict whether the change in entropy is positive or negative. Finally, predict whether the reaction will be spontaneous or not from the sign of the Gibbs free energy change.

TIME OF DEATH: WHEN DID IT HAPPEN?

Physical observation methods such as body temperature, post-mortem staining, and rigor-mortis are used to gain a rough estimate of time of death.[1] However, these indicators are not very accurate in their estimation of time of death, and can sometimes be contradictory. What is needed is a technique that can more precisely measure the elapsed time since death. Some recent developments include analyzing the serum concentration of Na^+ and lysine in the body.[1,2]

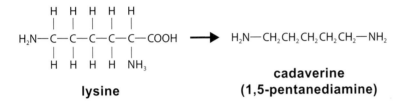

After death, serum sodium ion and lysine concentrations decrease. The amount of Na^+ decreases because the person no longer consumes sodium-containing substances and the kidneys are no longer functioning. Lysine is decarboxylated to form cadaverine and CO_2.[2] It is the production of cadaverine, along with other compounds, that causes decaying bodies to have such a foul odor. In this activity you will compare the time of death determinations for a homicide victim, Mr. Pink, using both the Na^+ and lysine methods.

PREREQUISITE KNOWLEDGE

Before beginning this activity, you should be able to

- Graph concentrations of reactants and products of reactions as function of time
- Use graphs to determine if a reaction exhibits zero, first, or second order kinetics
- Determine the rate constant for a reaction from kinetic data, including appropriate units
- Write the rate law for a reaction based on experimental data
- Select and use the appropriate integrated rate equation

APPLYING YOUR NEW SKILLS

After completing this activity, you should be able to

- Predict concentrations of Na^+ and lysine at any time after death occurs
- Predict concentrations of compounds of interest versus time from kinetic data in a variety of applications

Contributed by Brett Simpson and Austin Hitt, Coastal Carolina University
Revised by Cheryl Coolidge, Colby-Sawyer College, and Darlene Slusher and John Goodwin, Coastal Carolina University

THE PROBLEM

Early Thursday morning, Mr. Pink was found dead at the side of a deserted stretch of country road. Medical Examiner Quincy picked up the body and brought it back to the morgue. He concluded that the cause of death was a gun shot wound to the chest. However, he is unsure *when* the murder took place. Quincy turns the case over to his assistant...you! Your job is to determine the time of death.

Because he may be asked to testify in court, Quincy requires that you use two different methods to corroborate the time of death and that your analysis be as accurate as possible with each method. He provides you with standard calibration data relating the sodium ion and lysine concentrations to the time elapsed since death occurred (Tables 1 and 2). As instructed by Quincy, you measure Mr. Pink's serum sodium ion and lysine levels at 6:00 a.m. and obtain the following results: the Na^+ ion concentration in Mr. Pink's blood serum is 125.4 mM (mmol/L) and the amount of free lysine found in the body is 0.027 mM.

Table 1 Sodium Ion Calibration

Sodium ion concentrations following death. This reaction is zero order. Plot the data to obtain the rate constant for this reaction.

Time (hours)	[Na⁺], (mM)
5.16	128.06
9.95	125.95
15.44	124.07
21.51	120.88
26.73	118.92
33.87	115.88
39.09	114.02
45.06	111.89
52.91	109.25

Table 2 Lysine Calibration

Lysine and cadaverine concentrations following death. Plot the data in different ways to determine the order of the this reaction and to obtain the rate constant for the reaction.

Time (hours)	[Lysine] (mM)	[Cadaverine] (mM)
0	0.100	0.000
3	0.0750	0.025
6	0.0550	0.045
9	0.0400	0.060
12	0.0300	0.070
15	0.0200	0.080
18	0.0150	0.085
21	0.0090	0.091
24	0.0080	0.092
27	0.0060	0.094
30	0.0050	0.095

![icon] SOLVE THE PROBLEM AND DOCUMENT YOUR SOLUTION

Name: _____

Other Team Members: _____

Date: _____   Activity Title: _____

Level of Help used to solve this problem by the team: *none* ☐   *Au* ☐   *Ag* ☐   *Cu* ☐

Work with your team to solve the problem. Your instructor can provide three levels of help called gold, silver, and copper. *Au Help* presents a strategy that resembles the way experts think when they solve problems. The use of this strategy is illustrated and prompted to different degrees in *Ag Help* and *Cu Help*. As the semester progresses, you should move through these stages of *Help* to grow your problem solving skills. Your instructor will tell you what you need to do to document your solution. One method would be to provide the information requested in *Au Help*.

❓ DOES YOUR ANSWER MAKE SENSE?

1. Do your two results agree with each other well enough to pin a suspect down at a particular time?

2. Is there anything about the quality of the data that would lead you to trust one method over the other? If so, explain. If not, how would you decide the time of death to report in a way that you could best defend it, if you were called to testify in court?

BUILDING YOUR PROBLEM-SOLVING SKILLS

You will be able to complete the *Got It!* section, which comes next, more efficiently, and you will do better on exams if you take a few minutes now to improve your problem-solving skills. Communicating the steps in your problem solution to others and thinking back on the problem that you just completed will help you to improve.

1. Share your team's problem solution with your class as called upon by the instructor.

2. Identify the most important thing you learned about problem solving today that will help you solve new problems.

3. Consider whether you could solve this problem using a more efficient procedure so you can answer a similar exam question more quickly. If you find one, describe this more efficient procedure.

4. Identify whether there are any issues or assumptions contained in the problem and its solution that would limit using the same procedure for other problems.

5. Identify features of this problem and its solution that could apply to other problems.

1. Suppose that you did not find Mr. Pink until 22.0 hours after his death. Based on integrated rate equations, what would you expect his Na^+ level to be? His lysine level?

2. Before you stock a backyard pond with trout, you have the water analyzed to check for contamination. You find that the pond contains a chemical that is toxic. You call the local Department of Fish and Game and they inform you that adding certain bacteria to your pond will decompose this chemical and make it nontoxic. They tell you the amount of bacteria to add and that the rate constant for the decomposition then will be 0.41 month^{-1}, but they fail to tell you whether the decomposition is zero, first, or second order. If the concentration of this chemical in your pond is 1.34 M, and trout can survive at a concentration of 0.20 M, how long will it be until you can stock your pond?

REFERENCES

[1]Singh, D. et al. Linearization of the relationship between serum sodium, potassium concentration, their ratio and time since death in Chandigarh zone of north-west India. *Forensic Science International* **2002**, *130*, 1-7.

[2]Haglund, W.D., Sorg, M.H., Eds. *Forensic Taphonomy: The Postmortem Fate of Human Remains* [Online]; CRC Press LLC: Boca Raton, FL, 1997; p. 100.

ACTIVITY 15

BREATH-ALCOHOL ANALYSIS

The breath analysis test used by police provides a quantitative measure of intoxication and is critical in the determination of DUI arrests. In this activity you will examine the scientific basis of the correlation between alcohol concentration in breath and blood alcohol levels. The most common breath analysis measurement used by police makes use of Henry's law that describes the relationship between the pressure of a gas and its concentration in solution under specific conditions.

 ## PREREQUISITE KNOWLEDGE

Before beginning this activity, you should be able to

- Predict whether the solubility of gases in liquid solutions increases or decreases with increasing temperature

- Define molarity and use it to express the concentration of both liquid solutions and gases

- Express each variable (P, V, n, and T) in terms of the other variables in the ideal gas law

- Combine two algebraic equations to produce a new equation

⊚ APPLYING YOUR NEW SKILLS

After completing this activity, you should be able to

- Use Henry's law to determine the partial pressure and molar concentration of a gas in equilibrium with an aqueous solution of that gas

- Identify factors that affect the accuracy and reliability of a breath-alcohol analysis

Contributed by John Goodwin (v10), Coastal Carolina University

© *POGIL-IC Project*

INFORMATION

The most reliable measure of intoxication is a direct measurement of blood alcohol (ethanol or EtOH) concentration, but this test cannot be conducted in the field. In most cases, the results of a "breathalyzer" test administered properly by a police officer on the site are admissible in court.

The breathalyzer test depends on the proportionality of breath concentration of alcohol, C_{br}, to the concentration of alcohol in the blood. This concentration in the breath, C_{br}, is measured in mole/liter (M) by the breathalyzer. To obtain the estimated blood alcohol concentration, C_{bl}, the measured concentration in M of the breath alcohol is multiplied by the "breathalyzer correlation factor" of 2100. That is, $C_{bl} = 2100 \times C_{br}$. It is assumed that the ethanol is transferred to the lungs at 34 °C in the calculation. C_{bl} is also related to the *partial pressure* of ethanol in breath (P_{br}, expressed in atm) by Henry's law in which the constant k_{bl} has units of M/atm.

$$C_{bl} = k_{bl}P_{br}$$

THE PROBLEM

As a forensic chemist, you have developed a new, fast, and reliable technique for breath analysis that measures the partial pressure of ethanol in breath, P_{br}. This is different than the molar concentration, C_{br}, that is obtained from the breathalyzer test, but related to that quantity. In order to use your new method, you must convert the standard correlation factor of 2100 used in the breathalyzer test to the Henry's law constant, k_{bl}, for blood at 34 °C.

Name: _____

Other Team Members: _____

Date: _____ Activity Title: _____

Level of Help used to solve this problem by the team: **none** ☐ **Au** ☐ **Ag** ☐ **Cu** ☐

Work with your team to solve the problem. Your instructor can provide three levels of help called gold, silver, and copper. *Au Help* presents a strategy that resembles the way experts think when they solve problems. The use of this strategy is illustrated and prompted to different degrees in *Ag Help* and *Cu Help*. As the semester progresses, you should move through these stages of *Help* to grow your problem solving skills. Your instructor will tell you what you need to do to document your solution. One method would be to provide the information requested in *Au Help*.

? DOES YOUR ANSWER MAKE SENSE?

1. Does your analysis take into account the temperature of the breath? Should it? Explain.

2. Does your solution have the appropriate units? Explain.

BUILDING YOUR PROBLEM-SOLVING SKILLS

You will be able to complete the *Got It!* section, which comes next, more efficiently, and you will do better on exams if you take a few minutes now to improve your problem-solving skills. Communicating the steps in your problem solution to others and thinking back on the problem that you just completed will help you to improve.

1. Share your team's problem solution with your class as called upon by the instructor.

2. Identify the most important thing you learned about problem solving today that will help you solve new problems.

3. Consider whether you could solve this problem using a more efficient procedure so you can answer a similar exam question more quickly. If you find one, describe this more efficient procedure.

4. Identify whether there are any issues or assumptions contained in the problem and its solution that would limit using the same procedure for other problems.

5. Identify features of this problem and its solution that could apply to other problems.

1. The Henry's law constant for alcohol in water is 190 M/atm at 25 °C. The density of vodka is 0.914 g/mL and the density of ethanol is 0.789 g/mL. The formula for ethanol is CH_3CH_2OH (molar mass = 45.06 g/mol).

   a. You have a sample of 80 proof (or 40% by volume) vodka in a brand new, sealed bottle. What is the partial pressure of ethanol in the air just above the vodka (P_{vap})? Assume vodka is just ethanol and water.

   b. What is the molar concentration of the vodka in the gas phase just above the liquid vodka?

2. The relationship between partial pressure and molar concentration relies on the ideal gas law, as you have seen. If you collected a sample for the breathalyzer test at 34 °C and stored it in a rigid sealed container that did not change volume and allowed the sample to cool to 20 °C before analysis, what would change and what would stay the same? Assume that there is no condensation of any vapor, and no leaking of the container. Explain your reasoning for each.

   Volume of the sample

   Mass of the sample

   Mass of the ethanol in the sample

   Molar concentration of the ethanol in the sample

   Total pressure of the sample

   Partial pressure of the alcohol

   The breathalyzer correlation factor

   Based on your answers, does it matter if the sample cools before the amount of ethanol in the container is determined?

"Lye soap" was originally made by treating animal fat with lye (sodium hydroxide) or potash (potassium hydroxide). In this process, called *saponification* (illustrated at right), the salt of a fatty acid is separated as the familiar soft, water-soluble solid. One commercial sodium soap of this type is Ivory®, a product of Procter & Gamble™, sold since the late 1800s. Many home-made soaps contain small amounts of sodium hydroxide, making them very caustic, so the popular advertising slogan for Ivory® soap, "99.44% pure," has real significance to anyone who has had a bad experience with home-made soap! Since soaps are salts of fatty acids, they are bases. Ivory® and soaps like it are intrinsically somewhat basic due to their chemical structure.

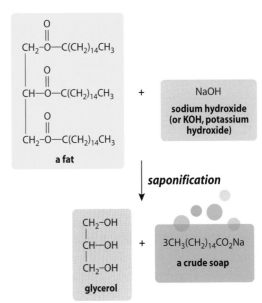

✔ PREREQUISITE KNOWLEDGE

Before beginning this activity, you should be able to

- Use pH to calculate hydronium ion concentration

- Recognize that the salt of a weak acid is a base

- Identify the reactions associated with K_a and K_b

- Use pK_a values to determine pK_b values

◎ APPLYING YOUR NEW SKILLS

After completing this activity, you should be able to

- Relate pK_a and pK_b values to relative acidity and basicity
- Determine the pH of solutions made from the salts of weak acids

Contributed by John Goodwin (v10), Coastal Carolina University

Organic Acid (source)	pK$_a$
Soya fatty acid (soybean oil)	5.6
Tallow fatty acid (lard)	4.6
Salicylic acid (oil of wintergreen)	3.0

Your small cosmetics and perfumes company is exploring options for making a new line of soaps. Some locally available sources of organic acids you're considering include soybean oil, tallow, and oil of wintergreen. The table at left lists pK$_a$ values you were able to find for these acids obtained by saponification. Several of your customers who have very sensitive skin have asked you to create a soap with a lower pH than that of Ivory®. A site on the internet states that moistened Ivory® has a pH of 9.5, as determined by pH paper held in contact with a wet bar of the soap. The Ivory® soap bar (classic) contains: "sodium tallowate, sodium cocoate or sodium palm kernelate, water, sodium chloride, sodium silicate, magnesium sulfate, and fragrance."

Your job is to determine which of the three locally available sources of organic acids would allow you to create a milder soap (with a lower pH), and to estimate what *that* pH would be at the same concentration as Ivory® soap in a litmus paper test.

![checkmark icon] SOLVE THE PROBLEM AND DOCUMENT YOUR SOLUTION

Name: _____

Other Team Members: _____

Date: _____ Activity Title: _____

Level of Help used to solve this problem by the team: *none* ☐   *Au* ☐   *Ag* ☐   *Cu* ☐

Work with your team to solve the problem. Your instructor can provide three levels of help called gold, silver, and copper. *Au Help* presents a strategy that resembles the way experts think when they solve problems. The use of this strategy is illustrated and prompted to different degrees in *Ag Help* and *Cu Help*. As the semester progresses, you should move through these stages of *Help* to grow your problem solving skills. Your instructor will tell you what you need to do to document your solution. One method would be to provide the information requested in *Au Help*.

? DOES YOUR ANSWER MAKE SENSE?

1. Would you expect the acid you chose to be a stronger or weaker acid than the one used in the manufacture of Ivory® soap? Explain why.

2. Is the pH of your soap closer to neutral than that made from sodium tallowate? Explain how you know.

BUILDING YOUR PROBLEM-SOLVING SKILLS

You will be able to complete the *Got It!* section, which comes next, more efficiently, and you will do better on exams if you take a few minutes now to improve your problem-solving skills. Communicating the steps in your problem solution to others and thinking back on the problem that you just completed will help you to improve.

1. Share your team's problem solution with your class as called upon by the instructor.

2. Identify the most important thing you learned about problem solving today that will help you solve new problems.

3. Consider whether you could solve this problem using a more efficient procedure so you can answer a similar exam question more quickly. If you find one, describe this more efficient procedure.

4. Identify whether there are any issues or assumptions contained in the problem and its solution that would limit using the same procedure for other problems.

5. Identify features of this problem and its solution that could apply to other problems.

GOT IT!

1. Which 0.10 M solution (a, b, or c) will be the most basic (i.e., have the highest pH)? Explain.

   a. 0.10 M Sodium acetate

   b. 0.10 M Sodium chlorite

   c. 0.10 M Sodium hypochlorite

Weak Acid K_a Values

Acid	pK_a
Acetic acid	4.74
Chlorous acid	1.92
Hypochlorous acid	7.46

2. Calculate the pH of a 0.10 M solution of sodium phosphate. Although a phosphate anion can react with 3 water molecules to produce phosphoric acid, H_3PO_4, assume only the first reaction to produce HPO_4^{2-} is significant because K_{b1} is so much larger than K_{b2} and K_{b3}.

   $K_{a1} = 7.5 \times 10^{-3}$

   $K_{a2} = 6.2 \times 10^{-8}$

   $K_{a3} = 4.8 \times 10^{-13}$

ACIDIFYING THE WORLD'S OCEANS

The world's surface ocean waters are currently kept at a pH of 8.1 by an H_2CO_3 buffer system.[1] As atmospheric CO_2 dissolves in ocean waters, it reacts with H_2O to form carbonic acid, H_2CO_3. Two researchers at the Lawrence Livermore National Laboratory, Caldiera and Wickett, predict that absorption of CO_2 from burning fossil fuels may cause the greatest acidification seen in the world's oceans in the past 300 million years outside of any catastrophic events.[2]

Coral in the Florida Keys Marine Sanctuary
NOAA Photolibrary www.photolib.noaa.gov

The current atmospheric CO_2 concentration is about 380 ppmv (parts per million by volume). The Lawrence Livermore National Laboratory ocean general circulation model predicts that atmospheric CO_2 levels will peak at 1900 ppmv around the year 2300, causing a maximum in surface ocean acidity that is expected to persist for hundreds of years.[2] Consequently, CO_3^{2-} levels are expected to decrease by up to 50%.[3]

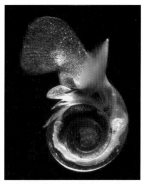

Limacina helicina, the Dominant Pteropod in Polar Waters
www.photolib.noaa.gov

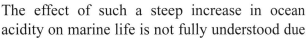

Coral in Chuuk, Micronesia
www.photolib.noaa.gov

The effect of such a steep increase in ocean acidity on marine life is not fully understood due to the complexity of marine food webs. For example, the loss of winged marine snails called pteropods would affect multiple marine food webs because they serve as a food source for many different kinds of predators.[3] It is thought that coral reefs and other organisms whose exoskeletons are made of calcium carbonate, such as shellfish and phytoplankton, are at the most immediate risk due to the decreased amount of CO_3^{2-} available.[3-6] A loss of corals would result in a loss of habitat for many marine creatures.

 ## PREREQUISITE KNOWLEDGE

Before beginning this activity, you should be able to

- Identify conjugate acids and bases

- Apply Dalton's law of partial pressures

- Determine gas solubility using Henry's law

- Solve acid-base equilibrium and buffer problems

- Correctly use the Henderson-Hasselbalch equation

Contributed by John Goodwin (v10), Coastal Carolina University
Revised by Darlene L. Slusher, Coastal Carolina University

APPLYING YOUR NEW SKILLS

After completing this activity, you should be able to

- Use the Henderson-Hasselbalch equation to relate pH, pK_a, and acid/base concentrations to each other

- Predict the effect on pH when a solution loses or gains an acid or its conjugate base in reaching equilibrium with the surrounding atmosphere

 # INFORMATION

- The solubility of carbon dioxide in water obeys Henry's law ($c_{gas} = k_{gas} P_{gas}$)

- The Henry's law constant for carbon dioxide in water is 0.030 M/atm at 20 °C

- The equilibrium concentration of carbonic acid in the ocean is roughly one thousand times the concentration of dissolved carbon dioxide under the limits of the question. That is, you can assume the carbonic acid concentration is directly proportional to the concentration of carbon dioxide in the air.

- Assume that the concentration of bicarbonate ion does not change appreciably over time because it is determined by minerals in the ocean

- The current pH of ocean water is about 8.1

- The amount of CO_2 in the atmosphere is 380 ppmv

- pK_a values of carbonic acid and bicarbonate are 6.37 and 10.33, respectively

- According to the Ideal Gas Law, the mole fraction of CO_2 in air equals its concentration in ppmv

THE PROBLEM

As a marine biogeochemist, you are planning experiments to model the effects of rapidly increased CO_2 concentrations on coral reefs. As you are designing your simulation, you realize that you need a simple model to estimate the pH of the oceans (and, accordingly, your experimental set-up). In order to validate your model, you will compare your results to those of Caldiera and Wickett. Use what you know to calculate surface ocean pH if the amount of CO_2 in the atmosphere increases from the current amount of 380 ppmv to 1900 ppmv.

SOLVE THE PROBLEM AND DOCUMENT YOUR SOLUTION

Name: _____

Other Team Members: _____

Date: _____   Activity Title: _____

Level of Help used to solve this problem by the team: *none* ☐   *Au* ☐   *Ag* ☐   *Cu* ☐

Work with your team to solve the problem. Your instructor can provide three levels of help called gold, silver, and copper. *Au Help* presents a strategy that resembles the way experts think when they solve problems. The use of this strategy is illustrated and prompted to different degrees in *Ag Help* and *Cu Help*. As the semester progresses, you should move through these stages of *Help* to grow your problem solving skills. Your instructor will tell you what you need to do to document your solution. One method would be to provide the information requested in *Au Help*.

? DOES YOUR ANSWER MAKE SENSE?

1. Should ocean pH go up or down when additional CO_2 is dissolved? Why?

2. Caldiera and Wickett calculated a pH change of –0.7 units. How does your answer compare?

BUILDING YOUR PROBLEM-SOLVING SKILLS

You will be able to complete the *Got It!* section, which comes next, more efficiently, and you will do better on exams if you take a few minutes now to improve your problem-solving skills. Communicating the steps in your problem solution to others and thinking back on the problem that you just completed will help you to improve.

1. Share your team's problem solution with your class as called upon by the instructor.

2. Identify the most important thing you learned about problem solving today that will help you solve new problems.

3. Consider whether you could solve this problem using a more efficient procedure so you can answer a similar exam question more quickly. If you find one, describe this more efficient procedure.

4. Identify whether there are any issues or assumptions contained in the problem and its solution that would limit using the same procedure for other problems.

5. Identify features of this problem and its solution that could apply to other problems.

1. Shellfish require carbonate to grow. What is the percent change in the carbonate concentration due to the change in pH that you calculated in solving the problem? Percent change is defined as one hundred times the change divided by the initial value.

2. A carbonic acid/bicarbonate buffer system also keeps our blood pH in the range of 7.35 to 7.45. If the pK_a of carbonic acid is 6.10 at body temperature (37 °C), what is the normal ratio of HCO_3^- to H_2CO_3 in blood with the average pH of 7.4?

3. Ammonia, NH_3, is a gas at room temperature. You may have had enough experience with a solution of ammonia to know that the odor emanating from the solution can be quite strong, indicating that the gaseous ammonia is lost from an ammonia solution in contact with air. If you have an ammonia buffer consisting of 0.10 M NH_3 and 0.10 M NH_4Cl, and it is left open to the air for several days, what would you predict about the pH *after* that time has passed?

    a. pH = pK_a of ammonium ion

    b. pH < pK_a of ammonium ion

    c. pH > pK_a of ammonium ion

    d. Impossible to predict

Explain your reasoning.

 **REFERENCES**

1. Hecht, J. New Scientist. http://www.newscientist.com/article.ns?id=dn4196 (accessed 4/09/08), Alarm over acidifying oceans, 18:00 25 September 2003.

2. Caldiera, K.; Wickett. M.E. Oceanography: Anthropogenic carbon and ocean pH. *Nature* [Online] **2003**, *425*, 365.

3. Orr, J. C.et al. Anthropogenic ocean acidification over the twenty-first century and its impact on calcifying organisms. *Nature* [Online] **2005**, *437*, 681-686.

4. Kleypas, J. A. et al. Geochemical Consequences of Increased Atmospheric Carbon Dioxide on Coral Reefs. *Science* [Online] **1999**, *284*, 118–120.

5. Riebesell, U. et al. Reduced calcification of marine plankton in response to increased atmospheric CO_2. *Nature* [Online] **2000**, *407*, 364–367.

6. Seibel, B. A.; Walsh, P. J. Potential Impacts of CO_2 Injection on Deep-Sea Biota. *Science* [Online] **2001**, *294*, 319–320.

ACTIVITY 18 THE COMPOSITION OF THE DEAD SEA

Since ancient times, bathing in the Dead Sea has been considered to be restorative to health. Today, this practice is claimed to be beneficial in improving skin conditions such as psoriasis, reducing muscle tension, and relieving pain from arthritis and rheumatism. Dead Sea salts are marketed and promoted as relaxing and healthful bath products.

The Dead Sea is the saltiest and deepest hypersaline lake in the world. The surface of the Dead Sea is the lowest point on the Earth's surface at an elevation of 417 m below sea level, so water leaves it only through evaporation. The concentration of salts

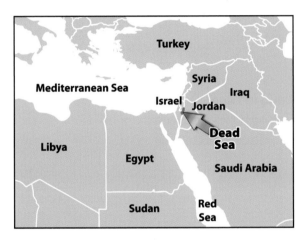

in the Dead Sea is so high and the corresponding density so great that people can easily float on the surface of the water. Deeper waters are more dense and saturated so that precipitation of salts occurs at the sea floor. Not only are the concentrations of ionic compounds much higher in the Dead Sea than in ocean water, as shown in Table 1, but the concentrations of cations and anions are not in stoichiometric ratios. This situation results because the ions come from multiple sources and precipitation equilibria remove salts from solution once the ion concentrations are sufficiently high. Your task is to identify the salt that is most likely to precipitate in the Dead Sea.

✔ PREREQUISITE KNOWLEDGE

Before beginning this activity, you should be able to

- Calculate molarity from concentration units of mg/L, g/L and g/100 mL
- Write the solubility product constant, K_{sp}, ion product, Q, expressions
- Explain why the solubility product constant and the ion product are different
- Determine values for the solubility product constant and the ion product from ion concentrations

◎ APPLYING YOUR NEW SKILLS

After completing this activity, you should be able to

- Determine the solubility of water soluble salts from the solubility product constant
- Determine a value for the solubility product constant from concentration data

Contributed by John Goodwin (v10), Coastal Carolina University
Revised by Candice Foley, Suffolk County Community College, and Richard Lumpkin, Lamar University.

INFORMATION

Table 1 Surface Salt Water Ion Concentrations in the Dead Sea in g/L

	Dead Sea Water	Mediterranean Sea	Ocean Water
Chloride	224.000	22.900	19.00
Magnesium	44.000	1.490	1.350
Sodium	40.100	12.700	10.500
Calcium	17.200	0.470	0.400
Potassium	7.650	0.470	0.390
Bromide	5.300	0.076	0.065

The total salt content of 1 kg of Dead Sea water is about 350 g.

Data from the Dead Sea Research Center

Table 2 Salt Solubilities (g/100 mL) in Water

	Chloride	Sulfate
Sodium	35.7	4.76
Magnesium	54.25	26
Calcium	74.45	0.209

Data from the Handbook of Physics and Chemistry

THE PROBLEM

Your task is to

- Use the data in Tables 1 and 2 to determine Q and K_{sp} values

- Then use these values to determine whether the concentrations of sodium chloride, magnesium chloride, and magnesium sulfate in the surface water of the Dead Sea are sufficiently high to form saturated solutions

- And finally identify which one of these three salts is closest to precipitating

Note that the moles of total cationic charge and moles of total anionic charge must be equal since the sea is electrically neutral. Assume the discrepancy in these totals is due to sulfate ion, which is *not* included in Table 1. Determine the concentration of sulfate ion needed to make the concentration of negative charge equal the concentration of positive charge. Note the molar concentration of positive charge from 1 M Na^+ is 1 M, but the molar concentration of positive charge from 1 M Mg^{2+} is 2 M.

![notepad icon] SOLVE THE PROBLEM AND DOCUMENT YOUR SOLUTION

Name: _____

Other Team Members: _____

Date: _____   Activity Title: _____

Level of Help used to solve this problem by the team: *none* ☐   *Au* ☐   *Ag* ☐   *Cu* ☐

Work with your team to solve the problem. Your instructor can provide three levels of help called gold, silver, and copper. *Au Help* presents a strategy that resembles the way experts think when they solve problems. The use of this strategy is illustrated and prompted to different degrees in *Ag Help* and *Cu Help*. As the semester progresses, you should move through these stages of *Help* to grow your problem solving skills. Your instructor will tell you what you need to do to document your solution. One method would be to provide the information requested in *Au Help*.

? DOES YOUR ANSWER MAKE SENSE?

1. Compare your K_{sp} expressions for sodium chloride and magnesium chloride. Considering that sodium is in Group IA and magnesium is in Group IIA, should they be different? Explain.

2. According to Table 2, which of the three salts is least soluble? Are your calculations of K_{sp} consistent with this observation? Explain.

BUILDING YOUR PROBLEM-SOLVING SKILLS

You will be able to complete the *Got It!* section, which comes next, more efficiently, and you will do better on exams if you take a few minutes now to improve your problem-solving skills. Communicating the steps in your problem solution to others and thinking back on the problem that you just completed will help you to improve.

1. Share your team's problem solution with your class as called upon by the instructor.

2. Identify the most important thing you learned about problem solving today that will help you solve new problems.

3. Consider whether you could solve this problem using a more efficient procedure so you can answer a similar exam question more quickly. If you find one, describe this more efficient procedure.

4. Identify whether there are any issues or assumptions contained in the problem and its solution that would limit using the same procedure for other problems.

5. Identify features of this problem and its solution that could apply to other problems.

1. Sodium chloride precipitates at the lower depths of the Dead Sea. What are the concentrations in g/L of sodium and chloride needed for precipitation of NaCl at these depths? To answer this question you need to assume that the concentration ratio of sodium and chloride ions are the same at lower depths as on the surface.

2. The Yucca Mountain repository, built for long term storage of nuclear waste, has long been mired in controversy. Though the date for opening the facility and accepting waste was set for 2017, as of the printing of this book, it is unclear when or if the facility will ever be used. One ongoing concern is whether the stainless steel nickel alloy containers holding nuclear waste would eventually be corroded by brine formed from evaporation of pore water (accelerated by the heat generated from nuclear waste decay). Alai, Sutton, and Carroll of the Lawrence Livermore Laboratory (2005) reported experiments which model brine formation based on the composition of Yucca Mountain pore water. One of the challenges is in obtaining reliable measurements of K_{sp} values at 95 °C. The results of the study indicate that the chemistry of brine formation is very complex, but demonstrated that one potentially corrosive ion, fluoride, is readily removed by precipitation as calcium fluoride. After evaporating some of the water from the initial pore water solution, the concentration of calcium ion was 1.25×10^{-3} M and the fluoride ion was not detected. The limit of detection of fluoride is 0.025 g/L. Assuming that this is the fluoride ion concentration, calculate the K_{sp} at 95 °C of calcium fluoride from these data.

REFERENCES

Maureen Alai, Mark Sutton, and Susan Carroll, (2005) Evaporative evolution of a Na–Cl–NO$_3$–K–Ca–SO$_4$–Mg–Si brine at 95°C: Experiments and modeling relevant to Yucca Mountain, Nevada, Geochem Trans. 2005; 6(2): 31. Published online 2005 June 7 Retrieved from: http://www.pubmedcentral.nih.gov/articlerender.fcgi?artid=1475789 (July 25, 2007)

Dead Sea Research Center, Retrieved July 20, 2007 from http://www.deadsea-health.org/new_html/general_main.html

Handbook of Physics and Chemistry, 53rd edition (1972-1973), CRC Press

WHERE TO BUILD AN ALUMINUM PLANT

The production of materials such as aluminum for use in industry and technology makes use of natural resources including metal ores and energy. Producing aluminum is very energy intensive because it is obtained from its ore by an electrochemical process at a high temperature. This activity focuses on the economic factors involved in locating an aluminum factory.

The Hall-Heroult process is an electrochemical method for the commercial production of aluminum using a cell like that shown in Figure 1. In this process, aluminum oxide (alumina, Al_2O_3), which is obtained from bauxite ore, is dissolved in molten cryolite (Na_3AlF_6) at about 1000 °C. The alumina is then electrolytically reduced at a carbon electrode to form aluminum and carbon dioxide. Since liquid aluminum is more dense than the molten cryolite, it sinks to the bottom of the cell, where it is siphoned off.

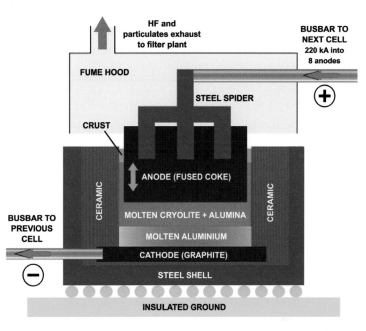

Figure 1 Hall-Heroult Cell (simplified cross section)

 ## ✔ PREREQUISITE KNOWLEDGE

Before beginning this activity, you should be able to

- Balance oxidation-reduction reactions

- Sketch the layouts of voltaic and electrolytic cells, identifying the anode and the cathode, and the reactions that occur at each of these electrodes

- Define the electrical quantities and units of charge, current, potential, energy, and power.

- Calculate the charge needed to produce a specified amount of material in an electrolytic cell based on the stoichiometry of the electrochemical reaction

◎ APPLYING YOUR NEW SKILLS

Upon completing this activity, you should be able to

- Determine the electrical energy required and associated cost for any material produced by electrolysis

- Determine the charge and energy that can be produced by a given battery (voltaic cell)

Contributed by John Goodwin, Coastal Carolina University
Revised by T. J. Anderson and Tom Gilbert

THE PROBLEM

Although several factors go into the overall cost of any manufacturing process, including labor and transportation expenses of both the raw materials and the product, the energy cost is an unusually important factor in the production of aluminum. As a chemical engineer working on a team to determine the location for a new aluminum plant, your task is to determine the minimum electrical charge required to reduce one metric ton (1000 kg) of aluminum, and use this value to estimate the minimum cost of the electricity per metric ton of aluminum produced in different states. Assume your company has narrowed the choice to one of four states: Pennsylvania, West Virginia, Ohio, or Kentucky, based on other factors. Your company has asked you to answer three questions. (1) Where do you recommend that the plant be located? (2) What will the cost of the electricity be per metric ton of aluminum produced in that state? (3) How much will be saved per metric ton compared to locating the plant in the state (of these four: Pennsylvania, West Virginia, Ohio, or Kentucky) that has the most expensive electrical power?

INFORMATION

- Assume 100% efficiency in the reduction process
- Only consider the energy needed for electrolysis; don't include the energy required to heat the cryolyte
- Assume the electrolysis is done using an electrical potential (voltage) of 16 V
- Electrical units are energy in joules J, charge in coulombs C, potential in volts V, current in amperes A, and power in watts W: $1 A = 1 C/s$, $1 V \times 1 C = 1 J$, $1 V \times 1 A = 1 J/s$, $1 J/s = 1 W$. Consequently, $1 kW\text{-}h = 3600 kJ$.
- Use the approximate energy costs in the United States shown in Figure 2 to determine the cost of electrochemical reduction of one metric ton of aluminum. This cost is a key factor in the decision about where to locate the new aluminum plant.

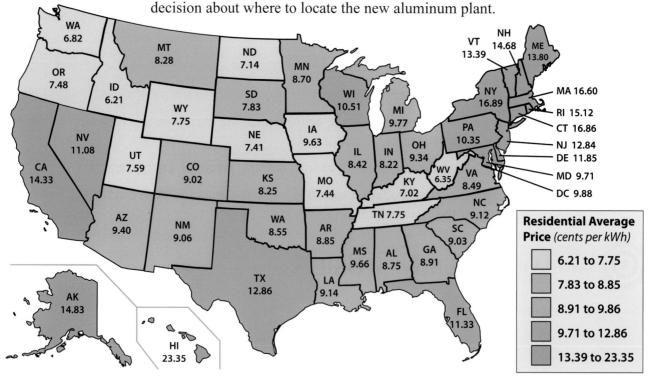

Figure 2 Average Cost in 2006 of Electrical Power in Cents per Kilowatt-hour
(*Based on information from Energy Information Administration, Form EIA-861, Annual Electric Power Industry Report*)

![checklist icon] SOLVE THE PROBLEM AND DOCUMENT YOUR SOLUTION

Name: _____

Other Team Members: _____

Date: _____   Activity Title: _____

Level of Help used to solve this problem by the team: *none* ☐   *Au* ☐   *Ag* ☐   *Cu* ☐

Work with your team to solve the problem. Your instructor can provide three levels of help called gold, silver, and copper. *Au Help* presents a strategy that resembles the way experts think when they solve problems. The use of this strategy is illustrated and prompted to different degrees in *Ag Help* and *Cu Help*. As the semester progresses, you should move through these stages of *Help* to grow your problem solving skills. Your instructor will tell you what you need to do to document your solution. One method would be to provide the information requested in *Au Help*.

1. Is your estimate of the electrical cost reasonable considering that the wholesale price of aluminum is approximately $1.00 per pound? Explain. (Note that the cost of electricity in producing aluminum must be significantly less than the wholesale price of aluminum if the producers are to make a profit since they have other expenses as well. If your estimate is close to $1.00 per pound or much larger, you should be concerned that you might have made an error. Another possibility is that aluminum producers need to negotiate a special rate for the electricity they use and can't pay the residential retail prices given in Figure 2.)

2. Did you take all of the relevant factors into account in your analysis? Consider the following list and identify which are relevant and which are not and explain why.

   a. electrical current used in the electrolysis

   b. the electrical potential applied in the electrolysis

   c. the time required to conduct the electrolysis

   d. the position of aluminum in the Periodic Table

   e. the molar mass of aluminum

   f. the charge on a mole of electrons

BUILDING YOUR PROBLEM-SOLVING SKILLS

You will be able to complete the *Got It!* section, which comes next, more efficiently, and you will do better on exams if you take a few minutes now to improve your problem-solving skills. Communicating the steps in your problem solution to others and thinking back on the problem that you just completed will help you to improve.

1. Share your team's problem solution with your class as called upon by the instructor.

2. Identify the most important thing you learned today about either the problem-solving process or a problem-solving skill that will help you solve new problems.

3. Consider whether you could solve this problem using a more efficient procedure so you can answer a similar exam question more quickly. If you find one, describe this more efficient procedure.

4. Identify whether there are any issues or assumptions contained in the problem and its solution that would limit using the same procedure for other problems.

5. Identify features of this problem and its solution that could apply to other problems.

1. In order to produce the hydrogen gas that is used as a portable fuel source in a hydrogen economy, it is necessary to initially use another stationary energy source. One way to produce hydrogen gas involves the electrolysis of water: $2H_2O(l) \rightarrow 2H_2(g) + O_2(g)$ $E^0 = -1.229$ V

   a. What amount of energy, in kilowatt-hours, is required to produce one metric ton of hydrogen gas by this process?

   b. How much more would it cost to produce this amount of hydrogen in Hawaii compared to Idaho? Assume that an applied potential of 12 Volts is necessary for effective reduction.

2. Aluminum-air batteries produce electricity from the reaction of aluminum with oxygen in the air. Such batteries have a very small mass for the energy delivered because aluminum has a low density and is the only reactant that must be carried when the battery is used in the air.

   The anode oxidation half-reaction is: $Al + 3OH^- \rightarrow Al(OH)_3 + 3e^-$ $E^O_{ox} = +2.31$ V.

   The cathode reduction half-reaction is: $O_2 + 2H_2O + 4e^- \rightarrow 4OH^-$ $E^O_{red} = +0.40$ V.

   The total reaction is: $4Al + 3O_2 + 6H_2O \rightarrow 4Al(OH)_3$ $E^O_{cell} = +2.71$ V.

   However, due to non-standard cell conditions, the potential produced by this cell is only about 1.2 volts.

   a. If you assume that the standard cell potential can be obtained with improved technology, what would be the total output of an aluminum-air battery, in kilojoules, if 1.00 kg of aluminum metal were consumed in its discharge?

   b. How long would such a battery keep a 60 W light bulb lit?

20 BATTERIES: WHAT DO YOU PAY FOR?

We all use common batteries, such as AA, AAA, C, and D cells for many portable electronics. Spontaneous oxidation-reduction reactions provide the electrical energy that we acquire from batteries. You may have a preference for alkaline batteries and a specific brand based on some catchy advertising. But, if you compare different batteries, what electrical or chemical differences are there, if any?

Alkaline batteries are based upon the reaction given below. Oxidation occurs in one part of the battery, reduction in another, and electrons are transferred through the external circuit from the oxidation compartment to the reduction compartment.

$$MnO_2(s) + H_2O(l) + Zn(s) \rightarrow ZnO(s) + Mn(OH)_2(s)$$

Technical specifications for *Energizer®* alkaline batteries are given in Table 1, and electrical units are defined in Table 2. Common abbreviations are m = milli, s = second, and h = hour. The electrical charge on N_A electrons is 96,485 C/mol.

Table 1 Technical Specifications for Energizer® Batteries

Size	Capacity mAh	Voltage V	Mass g	Diameter mm	Height mm
AAA	1,250	1.5	11.5	10.5	44.5
AA	2,850	1.5	23.0	14.5	50.5
C	8,350	1.5	66.2	26.2	50.0
D	20,500	1.5	148	34.2	61.5

Table 2 Common Electrical Units

Quantity	Name	Symbol (relationship)
Electrical potential	*volt*	V
Electrical charge	*coulomb*	C
Electrical current	*ampere*	A (1A = 1C/s)
Energy	*joule*	J (1J = 1V x 1C)
Electrical power	*watt*	W (1W = 1V x 1A = 1V x 1C/s)

Contributed by John Goodwin and Dick Bajek, Coastal Carolina University
Revised by David Hanson, Stony Brook University

© POGIL-IC Project

✔ PREREQUISITE KNOWLEDGE

Before beginning this activity, you should be able to

- Identify the quantities that are measured in units of volts, coulombs, amperes, joules, and watts

- Assign oxidation numbers to atoms in a chemical compound

- Identify the species oxidized and the species reduced in a redox reaction

- Identify the oxidizing agent and the reducing agent in a redox reaction

- Identify the number of electrons transferred in a balanced redox reaction equation

◎ APPLYING YOUR NEW SKILLS

Upon completing this activity, you should be able to

- Explain what is meant by the capacity of a battery

- Identify why different batteries have different voltages and capacities

- Determine the amounts of reactants and products found in batteries with different capacities

- Calculate the amount of energy stored in a new battery

- Calculate the time required to recharge a dead battery

THE PROBLEM

Your task is to qualitatively and quantitatively account for the differences in batteries. Do this by answering the questions in the next section.

SOLVE THE PROBLEM AND DOCUMENT YOUR SOLUTION

Name: _____

Other Team Members: _____

Date: _____ Activity Title: _____

Level of Help used to solve this problem by the team: *none* ☐   *Au* ☐   *Ag* ☐   *Cu* ☐

Work with your team to solve the problem. Your instructor can provide three levels of help called gold, silver, and copper. *Au Help* presents a strategy that resembles the way experts think when they solve problems. The use of this strategy is illustrated and prompted to different degrees in *Ag Help* and *Cu Help*. As the semester progresses, you should move through these stages of *Help* to grow your problem solving skills.

1. What are the units associated with the capacity of a battery?

2. Does the capacity of a battery specify the power, the energy, the current, the electrical potential, or the number of electrons provided by the battery? Explain in terms of the units.

3. How can you calculate how much energy is stored in a new battery?

4. Which electrical property doesn't change with the size of the battery? Why do you think this is so?

5. Which electrical property changes with the size of the battery? Why do you think this is so?

6. What chemical reactants are responsible for the production of electricity in the alkaline battery?

7. Identify the following species in the alkaline battery:

   a. species oxidized _____   c. species reduced _____

   b. oxidizing agent _____   d. reducing agent _____

8. What is the relationship between the mass and capacity of a battery? Explain.

9. How many moles of electrons are transferred through the external circuit for each mole of zinc that is consumed in the alkaline battery? Explain.

10. For each of the batteries listed in Table 1, calculate the total mass of reactants that is needed to produce the capacity for that battery. From your calculations, determine the percent mass of each new battery that is used to generate electricity. Summarize the results of your calculations in Table 3. Be sure to document your problem solving process in the next section.

Table 3 Analysis of Battery Mass

Size	Capacity mAh	Mass of Reactants g	Mass of Battery g	Reactant % Mass
AAA	1,250		11.5	
AA	2,850		23.0	
C	8,350		66.2	
D	20,500		148	

BUILDING YOUR PROBLEM-SOLVING SKILLS

Document the process you used to complete Table 3 by answering the following questions.

1. How did you visualize the problem?

2. How did you collect and organize the information?

3. How did you analyze the information to identify what you needed to find, the key information available, and the concepts or procedures that led you to the solution?

4. How did you solve the problem? Document your calculation in a way that is clear and understandable.

5. How did you validate your solution? Describe the evidence that your answer is reasonable.

Rechargeable nickel metal-hydride batteries have the following specifications. The redox reaction that occurs in these batteries is $MH(s) + NiO(OH)(s) \rightarrow M(s) + Ni(OH)_2(s)$, where MH is a metal alloy such as $LaNi_5$ containing hydrogen as H^-.

Table 4 Technical Specifications for NiMH Batteries

Size	Capacity mAh	Voltage V	Mass g	Diameter mm	Height mm
AAA	750	1.2	12	10.5	44.5
AA	1850	1.2	27	14.5	50.5

1. Why is the voltage of a NiMH battery different from that of an alkaline battery?

2. Why is the AA NiMH battery 2.25 times heavier than the AAA battery?

3. How much energy in joules is stored in a new AA and a new AAA NiMH battery?

4. How many grams of nickel hydroxide are present in a dead AA NiMH battery?

5. How many hours would it take to recharge a completely dead AAA NiMH battery using a power supply that delivers 100 mA of current?

Solving Real Problems with Chemistry

ACTIVITY 21

CHELATES ARE LIFE SAVERS

Many metals are an essential part of a healthy diet, but others can be highly toxic even at very low concentrations. The Occupational Safety and Health Administration of the US Department of Labor web site lists some of the more common toxic metals including cadmium, chromium(VI), mercury, and lead (http://www.osha.gov). Metals occur naturally in the environment, but may also be produced by manufacturing processes, poor waste management practices, and the smoke of coal-fired power-plants. Safe exposure limits for all of these metals have been established by OSHA.

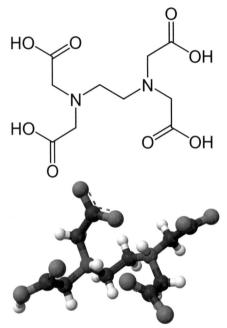

Figure 1 Structure of EDTA

Therapeutic removal of metals from the body of a person can be achieved by the use of **chelating agents** (pronounced *kee-late-ing)*. These agents are chemical compounds that form several coordinate covalent bonds with metal ions, creating a metal-chelate complex that can be excreted from the body. The word *chelate* comes from the Greek word for *claw* since its ability to form several bonds with the metal ion resembles the grabbing of an object by a crab's claw. One of the first chelating agents used was EDTA (ethylenediaminetetraacetic acid), although it now has been largely replaced by more targeted drugs. It also is used as a preservative in foods and in industrial applications that require removal of metal ions.

PREREQUISITE KNOWLEDGE

Before beginning this activity, you should be able to

- Write the equilibrium constant expression for a given chemical reaction
- Use equilibrium concentrations of reactants and products to determine an equilibrium constant
- Use an equilibrium constant to determine equilibrium concentrations of reactants and products

APPLYING YOUR NEW SKILLS

Upon completing this activity, you should be able to

- Identify appropriate approximations to simplify calculations of equilibrium concentrations given initial concentrations of reactants and products
- Solve a quadratic equation to calculate the equilibrium concentrations without approximation

Contributed by John Goodwin, Coastal Carolina University

As a medical research intern, you have been given the task of evaluating the use of an EDTA replacement, called REPL, for removing cadmium(II) ions from blood. As part of this evaluation, you need to determine the value of the equilibrium constant for the formation of the $[Cd(REPL)]^{2+}$ complex ion from REPL and Cd^{2+} in blood since the equilibrium constant is affected by the temperature, pH, and concentration of other substances.

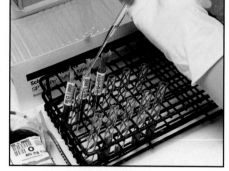

You add a known amount of REPL to a sample of blood containing 1.00×10^{-4} M cadmium(II) ions and then determine that the resulting equilibrium concentration of uncomplexed Cd^{2+} ions is 1.50×10^{-10} M. The data you collected from your experiments are in the table below.

Initial concentration of REPL	1.00×10^{-4} M
Initial concentration of Cd^{2+} ions	1.00×10^{-4} M
Equilibrium concentration of Cd^{2+} ions	1.50×10^{-10} M
pH	7.80
Temperature	37 °C

Use these data to determine the equilibrium constant, K_f, for the formation of $Cd(REPL)^{2+}$

$$Cd^{2+} + REPL \rightleftharpoons [Cd(REPL)]^{2+}$$

and compare the value you obtain with that ($K_f = 2.9 \times 10^{16}$) for the formation of $[Cd(EDTA)]^{2+}$ to identify which is the better chelating agent. In your analysis, assume that Cd^{2+} exists only as the hydrated cation or as the complex ion, and neglect the fact that Cd^{2+} can form complexes with the proteins and anions in blood.

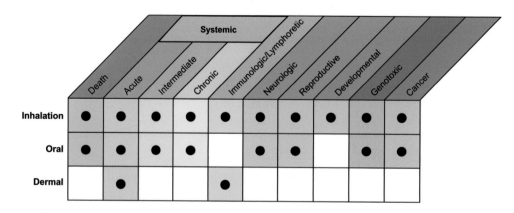

Existing Information on the Health Effects of Cadmium on Humans

Source: *Draft Toxicological Profile for Cadmium* from US Department of Health and Human Services (Agency for Toxic Substances and Disease Registry), September 2008

SOLVE THE PROBLEM AND DOCUMENT YOUR SOLUTION

Name: _____

Other Team Members: _____

Date: _____ Activity Title: _____

Level of Help used to solve this problem by the team: *none* ☐   *Au* ☐   *Ag* ☐   *Cu* ☐

Work with your team to solve the problem. Your instructor can provide three levels of help called gold, silver, and copper. *Au Help* presents a strategy that resembles the way experts think when they solve problems. The use of this strategy is illustrated and prompted to different degrees in *Ag Help* and *Cu Help*. As the semester progresses, you should move through these stages of *Help* to grow your problem solving skills. Your instructor will tell you what you need to do to document your solution. One method would be to provide the information requested in *Au Help*.

? DOES YOUR ANSWER MAKE SENSE?

1. Would you expect the equilibrium constant for an effective chelating agent to be large (much greater than 1) or small (much less than 1)? Explain your answer.

2. Is your answer consistent with this prediction? Explain.

BUILDING YOUR PROBLEM-SOLVING SKILLS

You will be able to complete the *Got It!* section, which comes next, more efficiently, and you will do better on exams if you take a few minutes now to improve your problem-solving skills. Communicating the steps in your problem solution to others and thinking back on the problem that you just completed will help you to improve.

1. Share your team's problem solution with your class as called upon by the instructor.

2. Identify the most important thing you learned today about either the problem-solving process or a problem-solving skill that will help you solve new problems.

3. Consider whether you could solve this problem using a more efficient procedure so you can answer a similar exam question more quickly. If you find one, describe this more efficient procedure.

4. Identify whether there are any issues or assumptions contained in the problem and its solution that would limit using the same procedure for other problems.

5. Identify features of this problem and its solution that could apply to other problems.

1. In examining another candidate drug, CAND, for use in removing Cd^{2+} ions from blood, an effective equilibrium constant for the reaction was found to be 5.0×10^{20}.

$$CAND + Cd^{2+} \rightleftarrows Cd(CAND)^{2+}$$

A dose of CAND was added at a concentration of 0.0010 M to a sample of blood containing 1.0×10^{-8} M Cd^{2+} ions. What would you predict as the resulting equilibrium concentration of Cd^{2+} ions?

2. What is the equilibrium concentration of Cd^{2+} ions when cadmium oxalate, Cd(ox), is dissolved in water to make an initial concentration of 0.0100 M? All of the cadmium oxalate dissolves but only a fraction of it dissociates as indicated below. What are the equilibrium concentrations of the three species shown in the reaction equation below?

$$Cd(ox) \rightleftarrows Cd^{2+} + ox^{2-} \quad K = 2.0 \times 10^{-4}$$

NASA's robotic Mars Exploration Rovers, *Spirit* and *Opportunity* are outfitted with a number of scientific instruments for analyzing the Martian surface. Three different spectrometers using interactions of electromagnetic radiation and matter analyze surface minerals. One of these is the Mössbauer Spectro-meter, which is used for many types of experiments involving the structures of iron and is well-suited to this application of studying iron-bearing minerals. Because this instrument is so specialized, it can determine the composition and abundance of these minerals to a high level of accuracy. The identification of the mineral goethite in the Martian surface is especially important since its presence is strongly linked to the previous presence of water. A Mössbauer spectrum indicating the presence of goethite is shown in the figure at right.

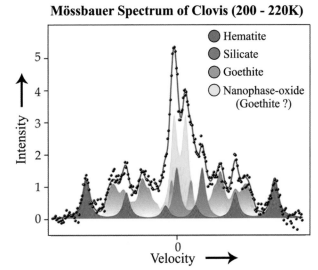

Image courtesy of NASA/JPL/University of Mainz

This activity focuses on the use of a gamma-ray (γ-ray) source containing cobalt-57, which is needed in Mössbauer spectroscopy to excite the nucleus of an iron-57 atom in a sample.

✓ PREREQUISITE KNOWLEDGE

Before beginning this activity, you should be able to

- Determine a rate constant from the half life of a radioactive substance

- Relate the rate constant for radioactive decay and fraction of radioactive substance remaining to the time over which the decay has occurred

◎ APPLYING YOUR NEW SKILLS

After completing this activity, you should be able to

- Find the length of time required for a sample of cobalt-57 to be depleted to a specific fraction of its original mass

- Determine the amount of radioactive substance that is needed to power a device for a specific period of time

Contributed by John Goodwin, Coastal Carolina University
Revised by David Hanson, Stony Brook University

The useful lifetime of the Mössbauer Spectrometer on a Rover depends on the lifetime of the emission of gamma rays at a particular minimum level by a 10 mg sample of cobalt-57. How long will the initial amount of cobalt be useful in the Mössbauer spectrometer? Radioactive decay is unchanged by temperature, chemistry, and environmental conditions. Your goal is to determine the length of time that the Mössbauer spectrophotometer on the Mars Rover can continue to collect data if it will no longer work when the amount of ^{57}Co remaining is 1 mg or less. The half life of ^{57}Co is 212 days. The time of travel from earth to Mars is seven months.

Artist's Conception of Mars Rover, Image courtesy of NASA/JPL

SOLVE THE PROBLEM AND DOCUMENT YOUR SOLUTION

Name: _____

Other Team Members: _____

Date: _____ Activity Title: _____

Level of Help used to solve this problem by the team: *none* ☐   *Au* ☐   *Ag* ☐   *Cu* ☐

Work with your team to solve the problem. Your instructor can provide three levels of help called gold, silver, and copper. *Au Help* presents a strategy that resembles the way experts think when they solve problems. The use of this strategy is illustrated and prompted to different degrees in *Ag Help* and *Cu Help*. As the semester progresses, you should move through these stages of *Help* to grow your problem solving skills. Your instructor will tell you what you need to do to document your solution. One method would be to provide the information requested in *Au Help*.

? DOES YOUR ANSWER MAKE SENSE?

1. Estimate how many half-lives it will take to reach 1/10 of the original quantity of cobalt-57. Is your answer close to this estimated time? Show how you made your estimate.

2. Did you answer the question that was asked? The spectrometer will be in storage during the trip to Mars. Did you take that time into account when calculating the "useful life" on the surface (i.e., the time during which the Rover can collect data)?

BUILDING YOUR PROBLEM-SOLVING SKILLS

You will be able to complete the *Got It!* section, which comes next, more efficiently, and you will do better on exams if you take a few minutes now to improve your problem-solving skills. Communicating the steps in your problem solution to others and thinking back on the problem that you just completed will help you to improve.

1. Share your team's problem solution with your class as called upon by the instructor.

2. Identify the most important thing you learned about problem solving today that will help you solve new problems.

3. Consider whether you could solve this problem using a more efficient procedure so you can answer a similar exam question more quickly. If you find one, describe this more efficient procedure.

4. Identify whether there are any issues or assumptions contained in the problem and its solution that would limit using the same procedure for other problems.

5. Identify features of this problem and its solution that could apply to other problems.

1. What initial mass of cobalt-57 would be required to make the Mössbauer Spectrometer described in this activity functional for 10 years on the Martian surface?

2. One type of home smoke detector uses a very small quantity of Americium-241, an alpha-particle emitter. The alpha particles ionize nitrogen and oxygen in the air to produce electrons along with N_2^+ and O_2^+ ions. The battery is used to create an electric field within the chamber, which causes the electrons and ions to migrate to the respective poles, creating a small current. When smoke enters the chamber, the airborne particles react with the ions, disrupting the flow of current and causing the alarm to sound.

   If a smoke alarm initially has 0.200 mg of Americium-241 as its ionization source, and has a useful lifetime of 120 months, how much ^{241}Am is required to create sufficient current for the alarm not to sound? The half-life of the isotope is 432 years.

Inside a Basic Ionization Smoke Detector
The black structure is the ionization chamber.
Image from Wikipedia

THE ATOMIC & MOLECULAR OLYMPICS

Atoms and molecules have many different properties, and molecules come in all shapes and sizes. Many atoms and molecules are competing today in our country's first annual Atomic and Molecular Olympics. There are ten events in our decathlon. Are you surprised, ten events in a decathlon? You will predict the winner of each event based on your knowledge and research of the properties of atoms and molecules. Unfortunately betting on the Olympics is illegal, otherwise you might win or (heaven forbid) lose lots of money!

 ## PREREQUISITE KNOWLEDGE

Before beginning this activity, you should be able to

- Convert a chemical formula into a Lewis structure
- Determine the three-dimensional shape of a molecule given its Lewis structure
- Identify molecules that are polar from their shapes
- Relate the polarity and other physical properties of molecules to their intermolecular forces
- Compare the kinetic energy and relative rates of effusion for two or more molecules
- Identify acids and bases
- Determine oxidation numbers of elements in compounds
- Determine ease of oxidation from an activity series of the elements
- Determine properties of atoms from their positions on the Periodic Table
- Calculate molar masses

APPLYING YOUR NEW SKILLS

After completing this activity, you should be able to

- Better explain the origin of various properties of elements and compounds

Contributed by Jill Barker, James Wood High School, Jamie Benigna, Roeper School, and Jennifer Stauffer, Hopkins School
Edited by David Hanson, Stony Brook University

THE PROBLEM

Your tasks are to

1. Predict for each of the following events which molecule will win Gold, Silver, and Bronze Medals.

2. Justify your prediction based on your knowledge of Lewis structures, molecular geometry, and other molecular properties.

The Events

Event #1 **Diving!**

Rules Molecules dive from a 10-meter platform to make the smallest splash.

Contestants sulfur hexafluoride (SF_6), carbon tetrachloride (CCl_4), hydrogen bromide (HBr), and iodine (I_2)

Gold _____ **Silver** _____ **Bronze** _____

Event #2 **Swimming!**

Rules Molecules swim 100 meters in a water pool (the molecules that have the strongest attraction to water will make the least progress across the pool).

Contestants C_3H_8, C_3H_7OH, $C_3H_6(OH)_2$, $C_3H_5(OH)_3$

Gold _____ **Silver** _____ **Bronze** _____

Limbo!

Rules Molecules compete with each other to see which can pass under the lowest bar by lying the flattest.

Contestants benzene (C_6H_6), carbon tetrachloride (CCl_4), phosphorous trichloride (PCl_3), octane (C_8H_{18})

| Gold | _____ | Silver | _____ | Bronze | _____ |

Event #4

High Jump!

Rules Elements compete against oxygen to determine which can achieve the highest oxidation number.

Contestants sulfur (representing SO_2), carbon (representing CO), chlorine (representing Cl_2O), and phosphorus (representing P_2O_5)

| Gold | _____ | Silver | _____ | Bronze | _____ |

Event #5

Weightlifting!

Rules Which of the molecules exert the highest vapor pressure to lift a weight at room temperature?

Contestants acetone ((CH_3)$_2CO$), sulfur hexafluoride (SF_6), methanol (CH_3OH), and water (H_2O)

| Gold | _____ | Silver | _____ | Bronze | _____ |

Graham's Dash!

Rules

Which molecule will race out of a really tiny hole in a container the fastest?

Contestants

hydrogen (H_2), carbon dioxide (CO_2), hydrogen bromide (HBr), and sulfur hexafluoride (SF_6)

Gold	Silver	Bronze

Event #7

Conformer Gymnastics!

Rules

Molecules compete to see which can contort itself into the largest number of different shapes (without losing any limbs!).

Contestants

pentane (C_5H_{12}), butane (C_4H_{10}), ethane (C_2H_6), propane (C_3H_8)

Gold	Silver	Bronze

Event #8

Wrestling!

Rules

This competition is fixed. The strong acid will come in first, the strong base second, and the weak base third.

Contestants

CH_3COOH, $HClO_4$, NaOH, CH_3NH_2, CH_3CH_2OH

Gold	Silver	Bronze

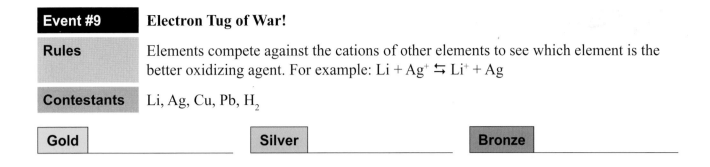

Event #9   **Electron Tug of War!**

Rules   Elements compete against the cations of other elements to see which element is the better oxidizing agent. For example: $Li + Ag^+ \leftrightarrows Li^+ + Ag$

Contestants   Li, Ag, Cu, Pb, H$_2$

Gold		Silver		Bronze	

Event #10   **Atomic Boxing!**

Rules   Atoms compete against each other; the largest atom wins.

Contestants   Mg, Ne, C, Si, Ca

Gold		Silver		Bronze	

 **GOT IT!**

Answer the following questions, providing a rationale for each answer.

1.   In the diving competition, which of the contestants would not be able to climb out of the pool afterward due to its high solubility in water?

2.   What would happen to hydrogen if she entered the diving competition at the urging of her boyfriend, helium?

3. In the limbo competition, would cyclohexane (another six-carbon ring) win, tie, or lose to benzene?

4. If propane were injured in the gymnastics competition, which of the following competitors would be the best substitute? Justify your choice to the Atomic and Molecular Olympic Committee.

   methane (CH_4)   octane (C_8H_{18})   hexane (C_6H_{14})

5. A lubricant company representative is at the Olympics looking for a new molecule that is non-polar, does not dissolve in water, and has a low vapor pressure so that it will not evaporate quickly. To maximize the lubricant qualities, the molecule should be relatively flat so that one molecule will layer on top of another. Draw a molecule that might fit what the company needs. Explain why your structure fits the needs of the company. (Then hurry and find the rep because she's paying a bonus for the best suggestion!)